Science and Christ:

A Dialogue

Richard Chiola, Ph.D.

with Sharon Zayac, O.P.

Hardcover ISBN # 978-1-959802-16-7
Paperback ISBN # 978-1-959802-17-4

The cover image, *The Six Days of Creation,*
by Hildegarde of Bingen (1098 – 1179).
Cover design by Corbin Design, Springfield, IL, 217-636-8175.

Biblical quotations from New American Bible, copyright by
United States Conference of Catholic Bishops

Dedication

In memory of Ann Regina Baker, O.P., D. Min.

1920 - 2021

Religious of the Dominican Sisters of Springfield-in-Illinois

Musician, Teacher, and Mentor

Table of Contents

Forward

If you are reading this, you have already shown interest in cosmology or Christology or both, and you will be greatly rewarded. Pass the word on to a friend or colleague so that they too can enjoy this experience. Not everyone may agree with every statement herein, but everyone who gives the book a serious reading will find it refreshing, filled with insight, challenging concerns, and scholarly knowledge about the cosmos and of Scripture. No one will be left unrewarded. Chiola is courageous, clear, and committed. His two loves, two emphases, are Jesus Christ and care for Earth.

Richard Chiola, priest, professor, therapist, with a doctorate in historical theology, has written this profound meditation in collaboration with Sister Sharon Zayac, a Dominican sister of Springfield, Illinois, a co-founder of Jubilee Farm, the sisters' eco-spirituality center. I have never met Father Chiola although I have known the Springfield Dominican sisters for many years. When Father Chiola asked me to write the forward to the book, I wondered why. I chose to do so, however, after a first reading, because it is a book that deserves a wide reception. The book will challenge us while at the same time make common sense. Whether one agrees with everything or not, they will benefit from it.

Little did I expect the book to be as masterful as it is. Chiola manifests an extensive knowledge of science and a keen appreciation of Christian thought. Unusual insight into the creation stories in the Book of Genesis provides one with a fresh perspective grounded in solid biblical research. It is exemplary in its witness to the constructive interplay between theology and science, how they differ, yet how they complement each other, how theology benefits from the interaction. It is this complementarity between the two that brings forth a new cosmology, a scientifically grounded theological perspective that culminates in care for Earth, one of Chiola's and

Zayac's primary concerns, as is true for Pope Francis as manifest in his encyclical *Laudato Sí*.

The author has familiarity with a wide diversity of authors. Paramount among these are of course Thomas Berry and Brian Swimme. His vision also resonates with that of Pierre Teilhard de Chardin, especially as he approaches the topic of Christology. He also shows appreciation for John Henry Newman's epistemology. As did Teilhard, Chiola sees an intrinsic and inseparable connection between one's theology of creation and Jesus Christ's role within it. As with Teilhard, cosmology and Christology are mutually complementary. Creation finds its fulfillment and culmination in Christ, the cosmic Christ, and Jesus Christ finds his consummation in the cosmos come to completion at Omega. Yet many other authors are also Chiola's interlocutors as well as many other topics explored.

His interpretation of the creation stories in the Book of Genesis manifest both hermeneutical skill and spiritual wisdom. The correlation between what science has unfolded and what Genesis teaches – their remarkable complementarity – emphasizes the interdependence of all of creation. What does dominion over Earth mean? – not domination, not lording over, but the administration of benevolent care – benevolent care being a significant theme, insight, and point of integration. As Chiola writes, "The truth contained in the Genesis myths is that humans are to sustain creation's interrelatedness and thus promote synergy, our collaborative working together with the rest of nature." The creation narrative presented here is a well thought out and highly integrated approach to creation as both unfolding and as God's gift Again Chiola: "Genesis also expresses the belief that human life was created to care for creation, as the creator continues to do, and to accompany creation to its fulfillment and ours."

I personally found illuminating Chiola's distinction between moral thinking and religious thinking and the evolution thereof, the former trait appearing with the evolution of hominins while the latter only with *Homo sapiens*. With the emergence of religious thinking, the human species becomes allured by transcendence. Chiola quotes research by Rappaport and Corbally's *The Emergence of Religion in Human Evolution*: "Religion is a non-obligatory neurocognitive trait of our species, *Homo sapiens*." The trait for religious thinking is the basis for the evolution of the world's religions. Religious thinking recognizes the numinous in our experience of the world. "The numinous is the source of our theological insight that creation exists because God desired to share existence," writes Chiola, once again linking the theology of creation with the evolution of the cosmos. The Christian, indeed every human, needs to be motivated to participate with science in the care of Earth and its creatures – one of the underlying emphases in the book.

Also illuminating is the treatment of the reality of death and its impact on us, both from the viewpoint of evolutionary science and from that of religious thinking. God did not create death to be the end of life. Death is a reality that pre-existed the emergence of the human species and the reality of sin. It opens the door to reflection on God's intention for creation, on the future of humanity and the cosmos. This leads Chiola, grounded more in the theology of Irenaeus at this point than that of Augustine, to bring to our awareness the traditional teaching on our divinization by the Holy Spirit.

Similar enlightenment will come from insights into compassion in contrast to competition, the role of empathy and how it has not yet been sufficiently integrated into moral theology, what neuroscience has to teach us as well as other religious or wisdom traditions, the evolution of sexuality and its purpose among us as relationship building, how we are called to be partners in being, whether as man and woman, or humanity and Earth, and the role and power of love in the unfolding of the universe, which did not emerge as a finished product, and in which God seeks us. It reminded me of something once said by Denys Turner in reference to St. Augustine:

10

It was not so much that Augustine was seeking God, but that God was seeking Augustine.

In our seeking we find God at the heart of the universe seeking us. God and the universe are in relationship with each other. Creation is not a part of God, but neither is it apart from God, nor God from it. This emphasis is at the heart of the universe story. God and creation are at one with each other. Here I appreciated an expression Chiola borrows from Rowan Williams, with which I was not familiar, with respect to the relationship between God and creation, that of a non-dual non-identity. God and creation are not two separable realities at this point, nor one pantheistic whole. All these insights are worth exploring.

Whereas many interested in new cosmologies do not see any connectedness to Jesus Christ as emergent within the universe, or many who are committed to faith in Jesus Christ show at times little interest in his cosmic impact, Chiola's passion is to bring these together, as he says, "This book is an initial attempt to present Christology in dialogue with the new story of the Cosmos." And he is successful. "Jesus was a cosmic event whose significance is on the order of a second Big Bang." This is just one line that struck me and stuck with me. Jesus Christ is an important part of the universe and from the perspective of Teilhard de Chardin an evolutionary leap forward.

At times Chiola becomes almost poetic in his descriptions and use of language. The book is challenging. Yet it makes so much sense. At times you may disagree. That is part of the dialogue to which it invites us. In the end, I think you will agree with its most basic intuitions. We are called to care for creation. God is not indifferent to the future of Earth. We too ought not be indifferent. Cosmology is incomplete without Christology, and vice-versa. The book is a needed corrective to thinking that is harmful, both to Earth, the universe, and to Jesus Christ, at least as Christ was understood by

St. Paul in his cosmic Christology. In reading, we will all learn something, and we will enjoy what we read.

Over sixty years ago, Rachel Carson's classic book, *Silent Spring* (1962), raised our awareness to environmental concerns. Most recently the same has been done by Pope Francis. Chiola and Zayac draw our attention to the same concern and integrate into a whole the relationship between Christ and the Cosmos in such a way that one cannot fully appreciate or understand one without the other. This is not just another book about Jesus, nor another about a new story of the universe, but a well thought out, highly integrated, well researched, much needed Christian cosmological vision. The authors have built important bridges which have significant consequences for our future and the future of Earth. May the God of all creation bless them abundantly.

Donald J. Goergen, O.P.

Author's Acknowledgements

A question sparked my writing this book. As Sharon Zayac, O.P., presented one of her programs on Cosmology, the story of the Cosmos and its implications for life and faith, one participant asked, "Can you elaborate how we and Jesus are different, if Jesus and we are both human and divine?" Sharon answered that she could not adequately respond, as she herself, like others, was still pondering that mystery. That interaction was the spark for this book. While I knew a little about cosmology, Sharon had studied and taught cosmology for thirty years. I studied and taught theology for over fifty years, and I was intrigued about writing on the relationship between Christ and the New Story of Creation. A member of her community suggested we work together. We have dedicated this book to her memory.

Cosmology over the last fifty years has developed from a science based in physics and astronomy into a philosophy of the natural world. I hope this book will help those who know a little about cosmology to expand their understanding of how cosmology and our religious faith can work together. For that purpose, I want to show how teachings about Jesus the Christ are given greater clarity through the newly developing cosmology that science is offering the human family. As Sharon says, "It is our creation stories that provide the context for understanding who we are, how we relate to the whole, how we come to understand the Divine, particularly as we delve into the meaning of our faith in Jesus the Christ. The cosmology being revealed to us through science tells us new stories about creation based in empirical data. This data must become the context for the whole of our theology. The new cosmology can help unwrap for us the meaning of Jesus the Christ in our present day." I believe her insight is supported by Christian theologians who from ancient times have said that nature is the first book of God's revelation. The second is Jesus the Christ.

13

How we humans have experienced the natural world, of which we are a part, has been and remains the context for all religious and wisdom traditions. Experiencing the natural world has been our only path for recognizing and expressing our religious thinking. I, therefore, have included some references to other belief systems, especially the Jewish roots of Christianity. In this way, I hope to be faithful to the vision of the Catholic Church expressed at the Second Vatican Council, that our faith is not alone in the world. Rather, we must dialogue with and accompany the abundance and varieties of human experience as presented by diverse sciences, philosophies, and theologies.

My hope is that our collaboration in bringing the perspectives of both science and theology to this book will enlarge the understanding of religious thinkers. We need to root theological statements in empirical scientific evidence, which is the created context for all divine revelation. I also hope that the reader will forgive my tendency to connect multiple topics and points of view, which may at times make it difficult to follow my thought. Finally, I want to thank Sister Sharon Zayac, O.P., for her patient and faithful conversations about cosmology, without which the project would not have succeeded, and for her editing of my writing, without which it would have been even more difficult for the reader. I also want to thank Fr. Michael Mascari, O.P., for his generous assistance with Chapter VII, the Rupture, and Fr. Donald Goergen, O.P., for his editing of the entire manuscript. Likewise, I am indebted to Barbara Reid, O.P. and Linda Gibler, O.P. for their endorsements.

In Peace,

Richard Chiola, Ph.D.

Introduction

Contemporary science and Catholic theology have very different perspectives on the Cosmos and so tell very different stories about the world. For this reason, the first chapter addresses the importance both of perspective and of storytelling. The chapter begins by addressing "science denialism." That is the popular myth that theology denies or at least ignores the empirical data of science. The chapter then turns to the importance of perspective, which determines what we see when we observe the world. From its perspective, science tells us that the universe is full of possibilities but there is no real purpose to it. On the other hand, theology seeks God in all things. The story theology tells is about the purpose for the universe's existence, which is its relationship with a creator.

While stories told by science and by theology differ, they find common ground in the contingency in the universe. Contingency means everything in the universe is dependent on other things. Theology and science agree on this. Science also says the Cosmos is indeterminate, which means there is no necessity for anything to exist or to exist as is does. But science is blind to the *why* of the universe because it concentrates only on questions of cause and effect, while theology holds that the creator had a purpose in creating, the motivation of sharing existence. Still, both science and theology work within a horizon of knowing and not knowing. Consequently, neither is as absolute as they may appear in their knowledge of the world or of a creator. Each can benefit from the perspective of the other, and that is the point we make throughout the book.

The first chapter spends some time showing how perspective develops, including the fact that our brain itself gives us two perspectives on what we observe. This is terribly important for understanding the way we get to know anything at all, but especially for the way we get to know ourselves in relationships with others. I will also introduce the importance of myth. Myths are wisdom stories about what humans have experienced repeatedly in creation, like birth and death. These myths function as the means of passing on from one generation to the next insights into our human experience. In the first chapter, I introduce the myth of creation that stands at the beginning of the Bible.

The second chapter examines the differing perspectives offered by science and theology on the beginning of the universe. The importance of this examination is to realize how both scientific and theological research interact from their differing perspectives and inform each other in telling stories about the Cosmos. Evolutionary theory initially concentrated on the process of natural selection among life-forms. But soon it was extended to the evolution of the universe itself. The progress of science in understanding how life-forms and the universe itself evolve has had great significance for theology. And theology also has influence on scientific research. It was religious thinking that first proposed the idea that the universe had a beginning, as we see in Genesis.

The Book of Genesis itself evolved over time. The editors of Genesis repurposed older myths to explain the beginnings of the universe. They created a story in which God is the source of both the seamless generativity of the world and the interrelatedness of its creatures. Just as we are still trying to understand the implications of the Big Bang, we need to understand the implications of the first myth of creation in Genesis. Both perspectives are important for our choice to sustain life on Earth.

Chapter three opens with the evolutionary history of human life on Earth. Science has made us aware that the universe is not eternal but has been evolving for billions of years, as has life on Earth. A close reading of the first creation myth in Genesis adds to our understanding of our human existence. Both evolutionary science and Genesis emphasize the unity of humanity but in very different ways. Science makes us aware of our interdependence with the rest of nature from which we evolved. Genesis explains the work we were given by the creator, to benevolently care for Earth and its creatures.

In the process of the dialogue between science and theology, something stands out as essential for both. As Pope Benedict XVI emphasized in 2009, in the encyclical "Caritas in Veritate," the book of nature is one and indivisible. If we want peace among humankind, we must protect nature. For this reason, I include here a brief discussion of homosexuality, which is a fundamental dimension of relationships in all societies across human history. My concern is that theological statements about homosexuality be rooted in the best empirical data available. That data increasingly indicates homosexuality is a human variant and, if so, would be part of the natural order of creation.

The fourth chapter is a close reading of the second creation myth in Genesis. This myth explains that our relational way of being is the source of intimacy with the creator, other creatures, and with Earth itself. No creature is simply its material parts. Each is made up of a unique set of relationships. We humans both define ourselves by and find our true selves in those relationships. Sex is integral to our relational way of being. That is why the chapter speaks of sexual differentiation and sexual desire. Sexuality is a created dimension of our humanity that moves us to intimacy in our relationships.

Science encourages us to recognize that our sexual desire is an evolved trait for the preservation of life. But it is also an evolved trait that moves us to care intimately for each other and all life. We are driven to act on our sexual desires by forces within us that are part of the natural world. We have learned through our wisdom traditions that our desires can lead us to act in ways that are not life-giving, and even harmful to ourselves and others. If we are to balance desire with the good of others, we will need more than one perspective. One to respect the good of our sexual desire and another to seek the good of both ourselves and others in acting on that desire. Only then will we truly function as life-giving partners-in-being.[1]

The work we have been given to do by the creator is the topic of the fifth chapter, the great work of caring for Earth and its creatures. The creation myths offered by evolutionary science and by Genesis establish us as collaborators with Earth and its creatures in this work. For this reason, Catholic teaching about land use and its preservation predates the current interest in environmentalism. But the current efforts of theological environmentalism are both interdisciplinary and ecumenical. Orthodox Ecumenical Patriarch Bartholomew is known as the Green Patriarch because of his long-standing commitment to teach our ecological responsibility. Pope Francis, and before him Pope Benedict XVI, have taken up the issue. As has Thich Nhat Hanh in Buddhist reflection, and the scientist Brian Swimme with his mentor, the Passionist priest, Thomas Berry. These activists and a growing number of others, including many young people, look for theologians to root their theological observations in the empirical evidence provided by contemporary environmental data.

Central to understanding this collaboration is the recent publication by Margaret Rappaport and Christopher Corbally, S.J. on the evolution of the trait for religious thinking among *Homo sapiens*. This trait is a unique neurological evolution in our species. The human trait for religious thinking is part of the material world. Its data must not be excluded by the material sciences from our understanding of the universe. This trait shows why early human observations of the world included the numinous, that which is beyond, above, beneath, around, and within the material world. Whereas science and theology once had appeared to be in conflict, we now see that the purposeful reintroduction of religious thinking

---

[1] For a definition of the term, partners-in-being, see Chapter X, section entitled "Encountering Jesus of Nazareth."

allows us to see Earth as a blue dot floating in space, where life is a fragile gift worth preserving.

The sixth chapter includes a discussion of three of the ten powers that mathematical cosmologist Brian Swimme notes course through the universe. These are allurement, cataclysm, and emergence. His observations about these powers provide a context for the observations of ancient wisdom about love, death, and the possibilities for transcendence in the universe. Chapter six is especially important as background to the reinterpretation of the original sin of Adam and Eve which shapes so much of Judeo-Christian religious thinking. That reinterpretation follows in chapter seven.

Chapter seven considers the rupture in human relationships that theology calls sin and its relationship to death. Any observation of our human situation must include sin, a rupture in our interrelatedness which threatens life itself. Sin threatens not only our personal existence but the very ability of Earth to sustain life. The Book of Genesis is well known for its story of how sin entered human experience. Interpretations of the myth have varied. The most familiar interpretation among western Christians is based on the idea that creation was ordered, complete, and static (fixed) prior to the introduction of the first sin by human beings. That interpretation holds that human sin introduced disorder and death into creation. However, we know that death was present in the world prior to the evolution of our species. Therefore, chapter seven introduces another Christian tradition about the fall of Adam and Eve that presents sin as a refusal to accept God's mentoring us to share divinity itself. This chapter provides the necessary background for a reinterpretation of original sin and its consequences.

In chapter eight, I have attempted to reinterpret the myth of the original sin by considering the evolution of human life on Earth. My reinterpretation relies on a close analysis of the third chapter of Genesis. How we understand sin, and especially original sin, is central to knowing God more truly. It also provides an explanation for the Incarnation, God's purposefulness in completing creation through Jesus the Christ. I think original sin was not a fall from a preternatural state of deathless and sinless perfection. Therefore, as Christian believers, we do not need to seek a return to original innocence. Rather, all sin is our purposeful refusal to struggle to achieve our likeness to God. Sin is inevitable for us, given this struggle that is part of the human condition. But sin is not necessary, if we cooperate with God's love at work in creation, the Spirit. God's love is insistently drawing us to divine likeness and is compassionate with our failures. Sin, nonetheless, is always tragic because it subtly fosters power over others and ultimately the use of death as an instrument humans use in the face of our vulnerabilities to secure our own interests.

The ninth chapter introduces Pierre Teilhard de Chardin's "Mass on the World." In his vision, the whole Cosmos is consecrated as a pleasing gift (a host) offered back to the creator. Teilhard's cosmic vision was founded on the Liturgy of the Eucharist in which Christ consecrates himself and those who believe in him as a gift to God. Teilhard widened the context of the liturgy to include the whole Cosmos, offered by all humankind with Christ to God. His language is not easily understood unless we examine the grammar used to speak about encounter with Christ, Christology. So, the chapter considers the biblical background for Eucharistic language, the problem presented by current doctrinal language about Eucharist, Teilhard's use of Christological language, and how our language about Christ might be put in dialogue with the new evolutionary story of creation.

Chapter ten reviews the development of Christology that was happening at the time Teilhard wrote his "Mass on the World." By the early twentieth century, Christology had become rather calcified rational assertions about the divinity of Jesus. While Teilhard was writing his "Mass on the World," theologians were developing a new grammar, one based on human encounters. This made encounter, rather than assertions, the foundation for talking about the humanity of Jesus. The various means for the encounter of Christ, like Scripture, Church, Eucharist, and the Cosmos are now the essential context for an ongoing development of Christology. Therefore, I return to the Gospels for some further consideration of how encounters with the humanity of Jesus reveal his divinity.

Chapter eleven reviews the previous chapters in order to lead the reader to the realization that our human consciousness is evolving as we seek the numinous in the universe. The humanity of Jesus of Nazareth has given impetus to that evolution in unique ways. Seeing the way he related to the world also provides some understanding of why Christians believe he is God's Word made flesh among us.

Finally, the chapter joins the insights of contemporary cosmology and ancient Christian writers to clarify what is meant by the Christian belief that Jesus is both God and human in one person. The Christian doctrine of the Incarnation is fundamental to the Christian perspective on the creator's intent for creation from the beginning.

Of course, the logical assertions about Jesus contained in Christian doctrinal assertions are clarifications of our encounters with Christ. But our encounters cannot be reduced simply to these assertions. It was encounters with him that gave rise to claims that the man Jesus of Nazareth is the unique Incarnation of the Word of God in the Cosmos. These claims were part of the earliest scriptural testimony concerning him. How does the ongoing development of Christology deal with these claims?

Chapter twelve answers that question by showing the relationship between the crucifixion of Jesus and the self-emptying love of the creator-God. Christ's self-emptying love on the cross is the likeness to God's act of creating the world, a second Big Bang. However, it took place in a fully human way. His death is the most profound evidence that Jesus was truly the Son of Man. That was his preferred title during his earthly ministry. It refers to the vision of the Prophet Daniel who saw a man to whom God had given the fullness of divine power. Christ's self-emptying love was that divine power. His human struggle to express it included his agony in the garden and death on a cross. As such, he was the Word made flesh, the divine code that codes the universe and moves it toward compassionate self-emptying.

The final chapter is about the last things, the end of the Cosmos and of human life. The perspectives of science and theology on the last things have significant differences. Science's take is rather bleak. Life on Earth is to end in five billion years or less. The Cosmos may either end in cold darkness or in fiery collapse in five hundred billion years. But science works within the horizon of knowing and not knowing. So, now there is data suggesting neither of those predictions may be correct.

Theology which is based on the data of cosmic evolution posits that creation was never a finished product. Instead, the creator from the beginning has been drawing creation to its fulfillment in God. Christian belief in the resurrection of Jesus provides the model for the fulfillment of creation, both of human life and of the Cosmos. Humans are the self-reflective part of the Cosmos who are to assist in the movement toward that fulfillment. We specifically are promised like resurrection to that of Christ as fulfillment of our existence. Created in the image of God, we are to share likeness of divine being, but as creatures and not as God. What that will be exactly we do not know. I like to think of it as being alive in the love of God forever, an adventure in coming to know the immensity of God who is our fullness and our wholeness.

The entire Cosmos and its various parts are promised a like transcendence because all creation was given the form of divine goodness from the beginning of its existence. This form or image can only be complete in God. But there are divergent understandings among theologians across the centuries about the ultimate nature of the transcendence of the whole of creation. Theology too works within that horizon of knowing and not knowing. What remains is

Teilhard's vision of the Cosmos on fire with the love of Christ moving toward the fullness of that love in the Heart of God.

Chapter I

Perspectives Matter

The Case of Galileo

Whoever tells the best story wins. At least for a time, until a better story comes along. A well-told story has the power to control further conversations.[2] Religion's supposed denial of modern science, or "science denialism," is a story about the relationship between science and religion. Telling that story usually includes a reference to the story of Galileo Galilei being put on trial in the early 1600s. His story centers on the politically powerful leadership of the Catholic Church insisting that sacred scriptures present an Earth-centered universe. Therefore, Earth[3] could not be both rotating on its axis and revolving around the sun as Galileo claimed. Four hundred years later, that story of conflict between Galileo and the Catholic Church continues to control the popular belief that religion denies, contradicts, or at least ignores the findings of contemporary science.

From his vantage point as a twenty-first century astronomer, Guy Cosolmagno, a Jesuit brother, and head of the Vatican Observatory,

---

2. Smith, Jeremy A. "The Science of the Story," Greater Good Magazine, June 8, 2016. "Experiencing a story alters our neurochemical processes, and stories are a powerful force in shaping human behavior. In this way, stories are not just instruments of connection and entertainment but also of control."
https://greatergood.berkeley.edu/article/item/science_of_the_story
3. Writing *earth,* without a capital letter, or placing *"the"* before it, further cements our thinking that she is an object. In our western capitalist culture, objects are here solely for our use, to give us what we want, need, or desire without reference to their own inherent value, integrity, and integral relatedness to all else. Spelling Earth without a capital E is indicative that she has no specific, unique, identity of her own, unlike all the other planets in our solar system, which we do capitalize. We have made it easy to dismiss our unique relationship to Earth, who is actually our greater self, an entity from whom we have come and on whom we must rely for every aspect of our living. By writing <u>Earth</u>, we subtly encourage looking at her differently.

tells Galileo's story a little differently.[4] He recalls that both scientists and Church leaders were divided over Galileo, some members of both groups supporting and others negating his claims. Some scientists believed Galileo's conclusions were correct and so supported him, but others knew he was not yet able to prove his claims and so continued to favor the then accepted Earth-centered perspective on the Cosmos. Key to the issue were telescopes, so new that scientists did not yet know how to use them accurately to make measurements of the stars, their size and distance from Earth. The science of astronomical measurement needed to develop further.

Church leaders also were divided, because even though his claims contradicted the scriptural Earth-centered description of the Cosmos, Galileo did not base his claims for a solar-centered system on an interpretation of scripture. Instead, he based his claims on observations of the stars and planets, some of which already had been confirmed as accurate. Galileo was simply claiming that his observations of the universe placed the sun at the center of Earth's movement, which challenged the accepted religious interpretation of the scriptures. He was not challenging biblical faith directly, but he was initiating a new perspective on Earth as part of a solar system. Therefore, Cosolmagno says, "We must be careful the stories we tell ourselves do not fit too neatly into contemporary stereotypes like 'science denialism'."[5] Careful or not, whatever stories we tell about the universe shape the way we see ourselves and our lives within it.

Cosolmagno makes another important point. While the findings of contemporary science are often treated as more absolute than they in fact are, scientists continue to disagree, as do Church leaders and theologians. As early as the 1600s, many on both sides of the issue recognized science would benefit from some respectful independence from theology, since each made its investigations from

4. Guy Cosolmagno, S.J. "What the story of Galileo gets wrong about the church and science," America, October 2020, 53-56.
5. Ibid.

very different perspectives. The growing independence of the material sciences allowed science to evolve from a static view of the universe toward a dynamic understanding. Three centuries later, this dynamism resulted in our realization that the entire Cosmos is in a constant state of evolution. At the same time, theology has incorporated the ongoing findings of contemporary science and necessarily has moved toward an increasingly evolutionary understanding of the universe and of our place in it.

Science and theology can and do influence each other. For instance, the theological statement that the universe was created and, therefore, had a beginning influenced some scientists to rethink whether the accepted scientific theory that the Cosmos was eternal might be false. That hunch resulted in scientists recognizing the signs of the Cosmos' beginnings in a Big Bang. Likewise, the scientific evidence that the Cosmos is evolving, and that humankind evolved from previous species, means that theology must rethink both its explanation of the creation of human beings and its explanation of sin and salvation.

The Differing Perspectives of Science and Theology

The differing perspectives of science and theology on the beginnings of the Cosmos and its end can inform and clarify each other. That is possible because in any dialogue between science and theology there is significant common ground in the contingency within the universe. Contingency can be understood as possibilities that cannot be fully determined before they show themselves. So, contingency means each thing's very existence is always dependent on something else. Whether something, like Earth, would come into existence cannot be absolutely determined before it happens; it can only be observed and evaluated once it happens. The reason Earth exists now is in part because stars eons earlier exploded and threw into the Cosmos the heavy elements of which Earth is made, elements like carbon and iron which were necessary for the

26

formation of Earth. But that is the easy part in understanding contingency.

Contingency also means nothing must exist the way it does; it could have been different. For instance, life has appeared to be rare in the universe, and the conditions for life to exist appear to be very narrow and specific, at least as far as we know on Earth and from what we can observe in the Cosmos. And that is not all. Eventually, things will not be the way they are in the universe because everything is constantly breaking down and reemerging as something new. Earth will have an end about 5 billion years from now when our sun becomes a red dwarf and incinerates Earth, and the galaxies may be nothing but cold darkness in another 500 billion years.

Because of contingency, science cannot find any necessity for anything at all to exist or exist the way it does. If everything that exists in this material universe is 1) contingent upon everything else that exists and 2) there is no scientifically verifiable necessity for anything to exist at all, nor 3) to exist in the specific way it does in our universe, then as Robert Russell comments in <u>Cosmology: from Alpha to Omega</u>, "there is no meta-scientific substitute for the concept of God."[6]

In other words, science simply says the universe is full of possibilities but there is no real purpose to it. On the other hand, theology establishes a purpose for the universe in a relationship with a creator. The Cosmos 1) exists because God wants to share life, and for that reason 2) the creator continuously sustains the Cosmos so that it will be brought to the fullness of life in God; and therefore, 3) Judeo-Christian theologies must always strive to root claims about God and creation in science's empirical understanding of the Cosmos where the purposes of the creator can be glimpsed.

---

6. Robert John Russell, <u>Cosmology from Alpha to Omega</u> (Minneapolis: Fortress Press, 2008), 52. For a full description of the role of contingency in understanding the relationship between theological and scientific perspectives see the whole of chapter 1.

Russell says, "The common role of contingency in both fields [science and theology] leads to a fresh perspective on why science and theology can be consistent with each other and need not be compartmentalized."[7] Theology and science do not have to be protected from each other, as if they are observing separate universes. Instead, the terms "creation" and "Creator" can be revitalized and filled with a new sense of joy within the new evolutionary story of the Cosmos. At the same time, science can be motivated to investigate issues first raised by theology, like the beginning of the universe and its end.

The reality is that both theology and science establish what they know within a horizon of what they do not know, and both use what we do know to make the unknown understandable.[8] The same contingencies were the basis for Native American beliefs about the Sacred Circle, Buddhist beliefs about the interdependence of all life-forms, and the Christian notion of mystical communion with all that exists. This common ground of indeterminate possibility allows the differing perspectives of science and religion to find some consistency in their interpretations of the Cosmos and our place in it. The possibilities within the universe are, for instance, at root in what contemporary cosmologist Brian Swimme calls the "Powers of the Universe."[9] His presentation of these powers seems to employ

---

7. Ibid.

8. Russell, see chapter 2, "The God who infinitely transcends infinity," for the contributions of mathematics and cosmology to the expansion of the ancient definitions of infinity.

9. The Powers of the Universe DVD with Brian Swimme: Seamlessness – the source of all powers, the ground of being, pure generativity; Centration – the power of concentration and exhilaration, how the Universe centers on itself; Allurement – the power of attraction, how things hold together; Emergence – the power of creativity, how the Universe transcends itself; Homeostasis – the power of maintaining achievement, what the Universe values; Cataclysm – the power of destruction, living in a Universe where things break down; Synergy – the power of working together, mutually enhancing relationships; Transmutation – the power to change the self, disciplines and constraints; Transformation – the power to change the whole, communion and intimacy; Interrelatedness – the power of

the perspectives of both science and theology. We will hear more about his work in later chapters.

The difference in the perspectives of science and theology is simple. Modern science observes physical processes and from those observations develops hypotheses that are consistently tested to verify them as accurate. Theology 1) observes relationships among persons and within the rest of nature, then 2) seeks to understand how these observations relate to the sacred scriptures, religious traditions, historical understandings, and current practical issues that science raises, thus 3) clarifying in an ongoing way our relationships with the creator, each other, and the rest of creation. In Galileo's day, science needed to gain independence from theology's perspective on the Cosmos. In the current historical situation, some scientists, like Swimme, are inviting theology back into a dialogue that may help clarify how the sciences can best preserve Earth and its life-forms.

How Perspective Developments

I learned something about differing perspectives on our common Earth as early as third grade. Seeing the white space between the green grass and blue sky on my art paper, the third-grade teacher asked me to look out the classroom widow. She explained I might notice land and sky met at the horizon. That was the first time I recognized my perspective could change. Up to that time, I had played in the grass and looked up at the sky, and these never touched each other. My understanding of perspective grew in stages, as first I was able to recognize the effect of the horizon in bringing together land and sky, and then eventually I learned how an artist can fool the eye and add "depth" to a flat surface, creating a three-dimensional scene.

---

care, how the Universe responds to the other; Radiance – the power of magnificence, how the Universe communicates.

Contemporary neuroscience has given us a new perspective on the human brain. We now understand that our brain is malleable, physically developing over the first thirty years of life. It is also capable of developing new interpretations of our experiences throughout our life. The human brain has two hemispheres, and each uses a different way of reasoning. These two hemispheres work together to clarify each other's interpretation of our experiences. One hemisphere reasons logically, which means inferring something that is not yet known from what is known. For instance, creating depth, which is a third dimension on a two-dimensional surface such as a painting. The other hemisphere reasons intuitively, immediately apprehending the relationship among things without logical reasoning or inference. For instance, for a child at play, the sky and grass never really meet. We play in the space between our experience of grass and sky. We often find our place in the world through an intuitive grasp of the whole to which we perceive we belong.

Modern scientific discoveries concerning the physical processes in nature, while most often associated with logical proofs gained through testing or mathematical reasoning, frequently begin with a hunch. Without an intuitive vision, sometimes called a hunch, there would be no theories to test and thus expand our personal perspective on the whole to which we belong. Similarly, theology is based on the intuition that the Cosmos exists in relationship to a Creator. However, the existence of God cannot be tested and thus verified. For that reason, many people object to theology being called a science as it was in previous ages.

Theology is frequently defined as faith seeking understanding. Clarifying theology (our talk about God) is not the same thing as faith (believing in God). Faith, because it is a relationship with another, cannot be solely an act of logical reasoning but involves an intuitive grasp of the whole person. In the case of religious faith, that intuition is that God is trustworthy. Nevertheless, theology's clarifications about our understanding of God can be verified as logical or reasonable, which is why theology was called a science in past ages. Because of eighteenth and nineteenth century emphasis on independent research and the autonomy of the individual, theology lost its medieval title of Queen of the Sciences. It is now classified as part of the humanities, like literature and history, all of which also comment on the physical processes in nature, but from a different perspective than modern science. Still, while theology and science emphasize different ways of thinking, dialogue between them is a good example of using both hemispheres of the human brain but in differing ways.

My eighth-grade teacher maintained that a student who looked out the window during class was likely to gain new perspectives and should not always be chided for inattention. She was encouraging contemplation among her students, a profound gaze upon what is present in the world around us or upon the world we carry within us. The perspective to which she referred was an intuitive grasp of the wholeness of things, coming to know oneself and one's place among the things of life. I have found that changing perspectives, logical cognition, intuition, faith, and contemplation are all essential for understanding the Cosmos as a whole, our personal lives within it, and especially our relationship with its creator.

These elements of my early Catholic education by religious women provided background for my preparing an introductory lecture when applying to teach undergraduate theology. I built the lecture on the similarity between viewing stellar constellations and reading sacred scripture. They have in common that what we see, while it appears as a single reality, is composed of parts that are vastly removed from us by place, time, and magnitude.

My analogy for the lecture was between Orion's Belt and the Book of Genesis. Orion's Belt appears to an Earth-based viewer as three stars relatively near each other in a somewhat crooked line. However, contemporary telescopes show the Belt is in fact composed of both stars and star systems at varied distances from Earth.[10] The differences in their distances from Earth and their individual luminosities means that the light we see as three stars left several locations at various Earth times.

Despite these differences of place, time, and function, as we gaze at the night sky, our unaided eye will see their light as a single image that inspired the ancient story of the hunter Orion. Contemporary astronomical research helps us understand the physical expanse behind the image we perceive and encourages us to wonder even more at the vastness and complexity of the physical universe we inhabit and into which we hope someday to travel. The stories we tell about our experiences shape the way we understand the universe and our place in it.

Perspectives Enshrined in Myths

As we know, ancient peoples did not have the benefits of modern scientific investigation. Instead, they were limited to their experience of life on Earth and the perspective it provided for perceiving the diverse traits in the universe. They developed profound insights from these experiences. Their imagination allowed them to enshrine their insights in stories that helped make sense of the world around them. These stories expressed their experience of the forces in nature and of the mysteries inherent in life and in death. We call their stories myths because they express a much fuller insight into human experience than would ever be verifiable by scientific experiment alone. These insights into human experience were handed on by ancient wisdom traditions and are even now shared by current generations. These stories are our heritage from ancient wisdom

---

10. The brightest star, Alnilam, that appears in the middle of Orion's Belt, is a blue supergiant 1,340 light years from Earth. At the eastern end of the Belt is Alnitak, a triple star system located approximately 736 light years distant from Earth. Finally, Mintaka, the westernmost star, is an eclipsing binary star approximately 916 light years from Earth; the two stars orbit each other. https://www.constellation-guide.com/orions-belt/

traditions. These myths continue to shape our understanding of the universe and our place in it.

The first chapters of the Book of Genesis (Beginnings) are such ancient wisdom stories, or myths. Myths are wisdom stories about what we experience over and over again in creation, like birth and death. Stories are the most ancient means of passing on wisdom about these experiences and their meaning. The myths about creation in Genesis are not pseudo-scientific explanations of the causes of Earth's existence, or theories about the origin of the universe. Genesis, for instance, says the universe was created in six days for a reason that is not strictly scientific. The authors wanted to convey their wisdom that creation has a purpose. Creation's purpose is that it finds its fulness in relationship with God on the seventh day, the Sabbath.

"Since on the seventh day God was finished with the work he had been doing, he rested on the seventh day from all the work he had undertaken. So God blessed the seventh day and made it holy, because on it he rested from all the work he had done in creation."[11] The Jewish editors of this text were a people whose covenant with God was to keep the Sabbath rest each week on the seventh day, so that they would learn to be holy as God is holy. Working six days a week sustains our existence. Being in the image of God is more; it is a relationship which requires time spent in communion. Sabbath rest for us humans is communion with God, even as Sabbath is God's communion with all creation. This communion-in-being is holiness, God's way of being to which creation is being drawn.

Ancient myths are often grand, epic stories told in an imaginative or symbolic way to reveal some fundamental truth(s) about the world and human life. Those who accept and retell a myth regard the truth it carries as authoritative. Thus, the myth will influence and even control future beliefs, attitudes, conversations, and behaviors, as have

---

11. Genesis 2:2-3.

myths about an eternal universe or a flat Earth. The Genesis myths are well told stories that describe the meaning, the *why*, of creation's existence and some truths about our place in it. Even earlier creation myths were told from the perspective of even more ancient religious communities who believed in a pantheon of gods. The authors of Genesis repurposed some of those myths in its first three chapters, taking the perspective that a single deity created the Cosmos and is drawing it to its completion.

The first three chapters of Genesis contain two stories of creation and a story of the sin of our first parents. Reading these myths, we could easily believe we understand their meaning simply based on the literal contemporary meaning of the words. For this reason, the creation stories have appeared to many to be a kind of primitive scientific explanation of the universe as the complete, static, and perfect handiwork of a divine creator. When we get to the third chapter, we find humans are the ones responsible for messing up its perfection. However, the meaning of these stories expands beyond pseudo-science once we become aware of their older mythic sources and the circumstances in which they were edited into the book we now have. As they were repurposed, these older stories established myths which would shape Jewish understanding of the purpose of humankind within creation and our relationship with the creator and all life-forms on Earth.

The Jewish editors refashioned creation stories which arose in the middle east more than a thousand years earlier. One, a Sumerian myth, is about the goddess Tiamat who created Earth from fresh and salt water. Her myth is at least 4,000 years old. The story fit the marshy location from which it sprang, Mesopotamia, which means the land between two rivers. A later civilization, the Babylonians, transformed Tiamat into a dragon queen of the waters, whom the sun god Marduk cut in half to create the sky and the land, separating the waters above the sky from those below the land. Contemporary cosmologists use her name as a metaphor for the stars that preexisted

34

our solar system and whose explosions sent heavy elements into the universe and thus provided for the formation of our Sun and Earth and neighboring planets. Instead of the halves of Tiamat's mythic body, these elements of carbon, iron, and oxygen were the scientifically necessary building blocks for our Earth and its life-forms. In the first story of creation in Genesis, we will see that the way the editors incorporated the Tiamat myth was critically different from the way the story had been told previously and leads to some important understandings for us in our contemporary culture.

There are two versions of creation in Genesis, both edited by Jewish scribes about 2,600 years ago. The Jewish people traced their heritage to Abraham and Sarah, contemporaries of the people who told the original story of the goddess of salt and fresh water. The Jewish people worshiped just one God and, therefore, had to reinterpret the extant stories of creation which contained both the actions of many gods and the relationships humans had with these gods. Editing ancient texts during and after their more than half-century of captivity in Babylon ending in 538 B.C.E., Jewish scribes tell two stories of creation's wholeness and one of its rupture in the first three chapters of Genesis. These stories begin with one God creating everything and end with humankind being exiled, just like the Jews were exiled from their homeland. The biblical stories of creation reveal the why of its contingency, its dependence on a creator.

Conclusion

Like the light from the various stars in Orion's Belt, the myths that have been edited into the Book of Genesis come from different sources and appear as a unified explanation of creation. However, once one is aware of the way these sources were repurposed by their Jewish editors, the Genesis story lends itself to a clearer understanding of the purpose of creation. Science asks *how* the Cosmos came into being, but Genesis answers a different question, which is *why* there is a Cosmos. In the next chapter we will examine the differing perspectives offered by science and theology on the beginning of the universe and the presence of human life on Earth.

Chapter II

In the Beginning

Perspectives Matter

This chapter examines how the perspectives of science and theology differ and how those differences affect the way we understand the beginnings of the universe, or what theology calls creation. The chapter begins with the material sciences and the Big Bang theory and then takes a close look at what the Book of Genesis says about creation. In this way, the chapter introduces the dialogue that is currently taking place between science and theology about the care of Earth and its creatures, which is called the new cosmology.

The new cosmology, the creation story being revealed to us through science, is essential for the continuation of life on Earth because it emphasizes our collaboration with Earth and its creatures. Of course, Genesis says care of Earth and its creatures is the task the creator gave humankind. As we saw in the previous chapter, both perspectives are important. New cosmology shows us that care of Earth must be cooperation with its natural systems and not construed arbitrarily as use of Earth and its creatures. The first story of creation in the Book of Genesis, if closely read, offers a similar message.

The material sciences behind the new cosmology examined 1) the material causes of things, like the flow of energy into matter and back into energy, and 2) the efficient cause of changes in the universe, like the explosion of a star through which heavy elements are cast out into the universe. But what caused life to evolve on Earth? The existence of life, especially human life capable of self-reflection, is contingent upon the fine tuning of innumerable physical conditions both in the universe and on Earth. The cause, the fine tuning of the physics of this universe which brought about life and human life, is understood by new cosmology as scientific evidence that the material universe has been in some way purposeful in doing so. This purposefulness is called the Anthropic principle which takes its name from our human race (*anthropos* in Greek) and its ability to recognize purposefulness in the evolution of life on Earth.

Earth, as far as we have evidence, is unique in the universe in that self-reflective life-forms have evolved here within the finely-honed physical laws which support them, laws which have a knife's edge balance. This causal fact is integral to the development of new cosmological science which integrates theology's understanding of the purposefulness of life and indeed all creation.[12] As the Passionist priest Thomas Berry wrote, "Within this [creation] story a structure of knowledge can be established, with its human significance, from the physics of the universe and its chemistry through geology and biology to economics and commerce and so to all those studies whereby we fulfill our role in the Earth process. There is no way of guiding the course of human affairs through the perilous course of the future except by discovering our role in this larger evolutionary process."[13]

The scientific evidence of cosmic evolution and of the evolution of humans, who are the Cosmos now self-aware, is the foundation for the Anthropic principle. The principle states that the Cosmos has been purposeful in the evolution of this self-awareness, which when understood in terms of the Genesis myths, could provide guidance for a larger evolutionary process of fulfillment.

Evolution, Species and Cosmos

The theory of evolution took its first large step with Charles Darwin's publication of *On the Origin of Species* in 1859, but Darwinism was limited to the evolution of living things. Among the theological issues that evolution presented for Darwin himself was why a Creator

---

12. Russell, pp. 46-52.
13. Thomas Berry, <u>The Dream of the Earth</u> (Berkeley: Counterpoint Press, 2015), 136. (orig. San Francisco: Sierra Club Books, 1988).

would allow so much suffering and death in the long history of the evolution of species. For religious-minded people the concern was also, if scientific evolution explained life on Earth, what need was there for a creator. Meanwhile, geology and anthropology were expanding the idea of evolution to Earth's very formation and to the evolution of human beings from the same more primitive primates from which chimpanzees and apes also descended. How could those findings fit with the belief that all was created by God and humans in the image of God?

Albert Einstein published his "Special Theory of Relativity" in 1905, in which his initial intuitive insight, confirmed by his mathematical equations, showed that the universe itself must be evolving. He famously (or infamously) fudged his own equations at first because he could not deal with the potential outcome, knowing it would change everything science then understood about the Cosmos. Up to that time, the prevailing scientific understanding was that the universe was eternal, having no beginning and existing in a constant state. Judeo-Christian theology had always held the universe had a beginning. Einstein's theory raised conflicts for scientists who wanted to compartmentalize science from theology in order to maintain its independence. While Einstein later admitted his lack of candor was the single-most critical mistake of his career, his theoretical equations caused research in physics and the other sciences to change exponentially. Einstein's theories allowed consideration of new domains for emergence in our understanding of the evolution of the Cosmos. However, as we will see, theological concerns among scientists would continue to affect their choice of theory, which in turn shaped their research.

One physical proof that the Cosmos had a beginning and has since continued to evolve is that clusters of galaxies are moving away from each other, which logically indicates they are moving away from an original point. A Jesuit priest, mathematician, and astronomer, Georges Lemaître, shares credit with Edwin Hubble for stating the

Hubble-Lemaître law, which posits that the farther a galaxy is from Earth the faster it is moving away from us. He published his paper on the subject in 1927, two years before Hubble's. Lemaître proposed that because the galaxies can be seen moving away from one another, the expanding universe could be traced back to a "primeval atom." Some persons thought this theory might be a proof of the theological claim of the divine creation of the universe from nothing. For instance, if the universe had an original point of origin, did it come forth from nothing, as in old creation myths, or from preexistent matter? And what was the cause of its coming forth?

Fred Hoyle, who was agnostic and believed there was no convincing proof for a creator-god, continued to hold the previously accepted scientific theory that the universe had always existed. His theological stance, that the existence of a creator-god was unnecessary, led him to believe a universe with a beginning was too much of a pseudoscientific explanation, too theological. Therefore, he rejected the modern scientific idea that the universe had a beginning and developed research to prove the previous steady state theory of the Cosmos. His effort was not successful. Nevertheless, he derisively nicknamed the expansion of the universe from a single point as the "Big Bang." The name stuck.

Hoyle also said that the theories of cosmic expansion and evolution which supported the Big Bang theory were as arcane as some Medieval theology.[14] For instance, according to the theory, it took a few hundred million years before there were sources of light in the universe, and we do not know for sure what exactly those sources were like. So, the universe was in darkness and a kind of chaos for a period at its beginning, as the laws of physics began to be expressed. That sounds like the version of the beginnings of the universe in the Book of Genesis. However, there was a more critical

---

14. John Horgan, "Remembering Big Bang Basher Fred Hoyle," Scientific American, April 7, 2020. https://blogs.scientificamerican.com/cross-check/remembering-big-bang-basher-fred-hoyle/ accessed April 20, 2021.

reason for Hoyle's comparison of theories of cosmic expansion to Medieval theology. That reason can be seen in the complexity of Steven Hawking's final theoretical solution of the beginnings of the universe.

While it is true that one's theological theory can influence a person's scientific stance, as with Hoyle, the opposite is also true. Scientific theories can shape theological stances. That was the case with the research of the great theoretical physicist Stephen Hawking (1942-2017) on the beginnings of the universe. Hawking's interest was in the fixed mechanical rules by which the Cosmos, he believed, operates without need for a creator. These rules theoretically were at play at the beginning of the Cosmos and continue to be manifest in its evolution toward some end, whatever that may be. However, the rules differ among small and large operations in the universe. The rules which govern subatomic matter differ from the rules for large structures like stars and galaxies. No one had yet explained how to reconcile these contradictory sets of rules. Hawking sought to do so.

The contradictory rules are the theories for quantum mechanics and for relativity theory. Quantum mechanics governs the dynamics of sub-atomic particles, and general relativity governs large-scale structures and their dynamics in the universe. Hawking ultimately tried to create from these two theories a single unified theory of the mechanics of the universe. However, these two theories remain incompatible with each other in our contemporary understanding of the Cosmos.

Quantum mechanics, refined by Einstein's relativity theory, states that in our universe, energy is never really lost but is converted. Relativity theory says that the way anything except light moves through time and space depends on the position and movement of someone who is watching. Perspective is critical. Hawking's perspective was that since both theories are now operative in the Cosmos, they were inherent at its beginning.[15]

Hawking never proved a unified theory for how everything in the universe works without contradiction according to these fixed laws of nature. Research and testing are still necessary if his last theories are to be proved. That did not stop Hawking from commenting on

_____

15. Hawking's operative understanding of the universe can be expressed by an analogy which can only be taken so far, the balloon analogy. The entire universe exists on a two-dimensional plane that is curved back on itself like the surface of a balloon as it is expanding. The universe has been expanding on this two-dimensional surface since the Big Bang. However, there is no center to this expansion, unlike a balloon, because there is no place where the expansion began or boundary where it ends. Based on this understanding of the universe, Hawking's theory stipulates the Big Bang would have occurred on a similar two-dimensional spatial surface.

Black Holes have a two-dimensional spatial surface called an event horizon. Early in his professional career Hawking studied Black Holes, a region of space/time formed by such intense gravity that theoretically nothing, not even light, can escape. Something inside would not be visible to someone outside. Whatever passes its event horizon is torn into energy bits, like erased data on a computer. The bits remain, but their meaning or history was thought no longer to be available. In theory a Black Hole could not radiate or lose its energy, and these energy bits could not be recovered. Hawking first showed that energy could radiate from a Black Hole, but then he was left with the question whether the history of those energy bits could be recovered. Hawking appealed to string theory to show that a Black Hole preserved historical information and would allow recovery of the history of those bits of energy as they were slowly released over time. Therefore, we could theoretically recover information from a Black Hole and thus nothing would be permanently lost in the Cosmos. He then turned his attention to the Big Bang.

According to quantum theory, Hawking understood, if one could turn back time to arrive at the moment of the Big Bang, particles would be foaming into existence and immediately disappearing as they do in a perfect vacuum. Nothing would have yet come permanently into existence, and so the universe would not have yet begun to expand. Just as at the two-dimensional surface of a Black Hole, its event horizon, we could not see into or beyond the event horizon of the Big Bang, and so we could not know anything prior to what was about to happen. Because there would be no cosmic inflation yet, neither gravity nor time, which are dependent on mass and movement within the universe, would exist. Therefore, Hawking believed at that two-dimensional surface it would be possible that the rules of quantum mechanics for subatomic particles and general relativity for astrophysical phenomena could be brought together into a unified theory.

the need for a creator. His final book *Brief Answers to Big Questions*, published eight months after his death, contains ten essays. In the first essay he addresses the need for a creator-God. He wrote, "I think the universe was spontaneously created out of nothing, according to the laws of science...If you accept, as I do, that the laws of nature are fixed, then it doesn't take long to ask: What role is there for God?"[16] His comment concerns God's non-intervention, not the existence of God as such. It is based on the principle that God may not intervene with the laws of the universe and yet remain the all-powerful being who created those laws. Any intervention would be considered correcting an original mistake, and presumably a deity does not err.

Robert Russell, a professor of theology, philosophy, and science, addressed this question of the need for a creator and offered a perspective based on what empirical science has demonstrated about contingency in the universe. He proposed the answer would be found in what he called "non-interventionist objective divine action" or NIODA. His theological explanation is that in quantum mechanics there is so much indeterminacy or contingency (everything depends upon everything else) that God could act in a direct, mediated, and objective way without intervening in the currently known laws of nature. He renamed his theory QM-NIODA in order to include the quantum mechanics origin of the theory.[17] In developing this theory, Russell remained faithful to his belief that theological claims must be rooted in empirical science when making statements about the ongoing creative power of God in the Cosmos. It helps to recall that both science and theology operate within the horizon of the known and the unknown. As science makes inquiry of theology, so one's

---

16. Audrey Barrick, "Stephen Hawking Explains Creation, Big Bang Sans God," The Christian Post, August 8, 2011.https://www.christianpost.com/news/stephen-Hawking-something-out-of-nothing-is-possible.html accessed April 20, 2021.
17. Russell, chapters 4 and 5.

theological stance can open new scientific possibilities, as in Russell's case, making room for ongoing divine creativity in the Cosmos.

The Perspective of Genesis 1

The Jewish editors of Genesis offered stories that unify the relationship of everything in the universe as the work of God who continues to provide a future for the universe. Things in the Cosmos are what they are because they exist in and for their relationship with the creator. The creation stories in Genesis describe why things on Earth are the way they are and have been from the beginning. While modern science also recognizes that everything in the universe is interrelated, Genesis has a vastly different perspective on those interrelationships, not mechanical causality but existence itself as relationship.[18]

Fundamentally, the Jewish belief behind Genesis is that creation is the work of a single being radically different from creation, who brought the Cosmos into being, continues to sustain it, and is bringing it to completion. Creation is the work in which God can be known, but creation is not God. God is present to creation as its creator, is in relation with creation as its sustainer, and God is also the promise of its future completion. Human beings are a part of creation, capable of conscious reflection, and thus function as the universe personally responding to God. This perspective on creation is shared by Judaism and Christianity, which grew from it, and by

---

18. In Genesis, the creator-God of the Jews is eternal; God's existence can neither be circumscribed within time nor excluded from time. God is both creation's formal cause and ultimate purpose. A formal cause provides the form taken on by a piece of art. As creation's formal cause, God calls each thing into a relational way of being which is the way of being that is God's own self. God is the formal cause of creation in which everything is known in its relationship to the creator and to other creatures. The ultimate purpose of creation, its final cause, is the promise toward which God draws creation, its future fulfillment in its relationship with God. God calls into being (creation from nothing) and continues to call all that is to its fulfillment (ongoing creation, sustaining the evolution of the Cosmos toward its fulfillment in God).

Islam, which interacted in its origin with both religions. Even Hinduism, which is more ancient than these three, holds much the same understanding of God's relationship with creation, although this is obscured in the public mind by Hinduism's vastly different expressions and practices.[19]

Genesis begins, "In the beginning, when God created the heavens and the Earth, the Earth was a formless wasteland, and darkness covered the abyss, while a mighty wind swept over the water."[20] "In the beginning" is an ominous moment, like the Big Bang occurring without prior time, without cause or explanation. But what then is the meaning of "*when* God created? There are multiple possibilities. Certainly, for Genesis "In the beginning, *when God created*" is a boundary beyond which only the Creator has knowledge. Many theologians say this "when" is before anything else exists, only the eternal God. But the next words offer another possibility. "The Earth was a formless wasteland, and darkness covered the abyss." Some theologians have speculated God created from pre-existing matter. It is an interpretation, resembling Hindu belief based on the theory that the Cosmos will collapse in time into an infinitely dense and hot point from which a new Big Bang could emerge. Just so, God created the current Cosmos from preexisting matter by destroying what previously existed in order to begin anew, like a subsistence farmer burning off the stubble before planting. But that is not the currently accepted theological interpretation among Christians.

It appears instead that "formless wasteland," *tohu wa-bohu* in Hebrew, is a literary device, the use of synonyms to intensify the meaning, "waste and void." Such a literary device can be interpreted in a variety of ways. For instance, in Greek mythology, the universe

---

19. Jayaram V, "Hinduism and the Belief in one God," https://www.hinduwebsite.com/onegod.asp, accessed April 20, 2021. According to the Amazon cite for his many publications, Jayaram V. is a leading scholar of Indian religions, philosophy, mysticism, and spirituality. His website is https://jayaramv.com, and he is a practitioner of santana dharmas.
20. Genesis 1:1.

comes forth from chaos (also known as formless infinity) which gives way to order as God creates. The Greek mind was the cultural context for the development of much of early Christian theology. It interpreted "waste and void" as chaos. Creation was then "order" or form given to the formless.

From a third perspective, that of the Jewish editors living in exile, waste and void could be an affirmation that their God is a God of history who creates a future for the Jews. As such, it would emphasize that the creation story is not simply about an event in the past, like their exile from their homeland, but about the creation of a future to which God is drawing a people. Genesis from this Jewish perspective declares that Earth and its life-forms have an unfolding historical existence. Today, we would say it is evolutionary. Genesis even places an image of evolutionary fulfillment at the beginning. As we will see in the next chapter, it describes a mythic ideal existence of harmony in the relationships between the creator and creation and among the creatures themselves.

The literary device, "waste and void," has yet another purpose. It repudiates the required mythic sacrifice of Tiamat by Marduk, who created Earth and sky from the halves of Tiamat's body. The God of the Jews does not rely on sacrifice in order to create. Here another word about myths is necessary. "Myths are value-impregnated beliefs or stories which bind people together at the deepest level of group life and which they live by and for. Myths are not fairy tales or fallacies. A myth is a story or tradition that claims to reveal in an imaginative or symbolic way a fundamental truth about the world and human life."[21]

Myths like that of Tiamat and similar myths in multiple world religions give divine approval for a system of scapegoating that includes human sacrifice. If the gods create by sacrificing each other, humans have approbation to copy that behavior in order to create

---

21. Gerald A. Arbuckle, Violence, Society and the Church: A cultural approach. (Collegeville, MN: Liturgical Press, 2004), 6.

their human cultures and secure their societies. All cultures and societies based on myths of victimization will attempt to create order where they perceive chaos by sacrificing fellow humans.

The research and writing of Rene Girard demonstrated that this memetic (copycat) system of scapegoating is found across our history among all human cultures.[22] Girard was an historian, literary critic, and philosopher of social science whose writing belongs to the tradition of anthropological philosophy. Girard showed that random victimization has an historical and global function among humans as cultures attempt to maintain cohesion and social stability.[23] Random victimization is selecting a victim to cast out of society or kill, like a slave or young girl among Romans, or prisoners of war among the Mayans or Aztecs, or as among the ancient Celts who selected someone to be king for a year to secure the fertility of the land and then sacrificed him at harvest to thank the gods. Notably, the Homeric myth of the defeat of Troy begins with the leader of the Greek forces sacrificing his young daughter in hope of the gods giving him victory over the Trojans.

Indeed, the human species has consistently tried to protect itself from the dark abyss of cultural and social chaos which inevitably threatens our human interactions. In multiple world religions and the cultures based on them, that abyss has been avoided by human sacrifice. But not in Judaism. The God of the Jews is the fullness of power who does not create by random sacrifice. The Jewish God creating without sacrifice struck at the lack of creative capacity of the gods of surrounding peoples who demanded human sacrifice. The

---

22. In Girard's theory, memesis or imitation occurs when one person's desire is mimicked by another. For instance, marketing strategy is to get us to want what the elites in society have, be they sports or movie stars. Cultures around the world are based on myths which are copied by the members of the culture. If the gods of the cultural myth sacrifice each other, humans mimic that behavior and human sacrifice continues.
23. Rene Girard, Evolution and Conversion: Dialogues on the origin of culture (London: Bloomsbury, 2008).

God of the Jews was the foundation for a religion and society based upon it which rejected human sacrifice. This rejection is the basis for the story of Abraham, in Genesis 22, intending to sacrifice his son Isaac but God staying his hand. The story begins with Abraham, the ancestor of the Jews, being told by God to sacrifice his son, which would be imitation of sacrifices among surrounding tribes. The story ends instead with God's intervention establishing animal sacrifice as the substitute for human sacrifice.

Instead of dependence upon sacrifice, God creates by sharing existence itself. In the beginning according to the Book of Genesis there was a void, the absence of created being, created existence. In the face of a void, God speaks, and by doing so, gifts shared-being to what formerly was simply "Not." The device of "waste and void" packs a particularly mythic Jewish punch. The Creator whose name was revealed to the Jews as "I AM" calls the Cosmos into existence in a relationship as "Thou."[24] Creation is not simply coming into being from nothing, but coming into relational being, and being-related holds promise for the future. This Jewish perspective on creation mimics and is a reaffirmation of their sense of themselves as being called into being as a people in relationship with God through the faith of their ancestor Abraham.

James Alison, a Catholic priest and Girardian theologian, says that during the Babylonian captivity the Jewish editors of Genesis had not yet arrived at the full meaning of this mythic device for the future of the Cosmos.[25] This relational way of being is now understood to be the case for all humans and indeed all creation. Genesis contains multiple founding myths for the Jewish people which are also claimed by other religions and by the many cultures based on them. As Alison reminds us, "In the mythologies of every group there will be

---

24. Exodus 3:14, the name "I AM" for the God of the Jews was first revealed to Moses as God sent him on his mission to free the Israelites from slavery in Egypt.
25. James Alison, Faith beyond resentment: fragments catholic and gay (NY: Crossroads Publishing, June 2016), 156.

founding myths that are the ultimate forces of identity and hope in the future. A culture will continue only if the founding myths are able to be repeatedly retold."[26]

Rabbi Dr. Abraham Joshua Heschel, in *God's Search for Man*, extended the ancient Jewish founding myths to establish for all humans that "an ultimate issue is at stake in our existence, the relevance of which surpasses all final formulations." The ultimate issue is the divine presence in search of a relationship with humankind. Heschel says there are "three starting points of contemplation about God," which are worship, learning, and action. And worship begins with, "Lift up your eyes and see who created these."[27]

The "Why" of Creation

In the beginning Genesis says, "darkness covered the abyss, while a *mighty wind* swept over the waters."[28] In Hebrew, *ruah* is breath, spirit, or wind; so, this passage may be translated, "the breath of God (*spirit*) swept over the troubled water." Without the breath of God, how can anything be alive in an I-Thou relationship? Without spirit can one ever see more than darkness? And so, it can be said that from the beginning spirit was integral in bringing creation into relational being. In the evolution of *Homo sapiens,* who are capable of intentional relational being, it became clear that the inward reality of the material world is spirit. As the world has evolved, spirit has been the inward power for its ongoing diversification.

Spirit exercises its power in lived situations. The situation in which Jewish scribes edited these myths included the fact that they were not only a community of exiles but a community at prayer, especially on

26. Ibid., 7.
27. Abraham Joshua Heschel, <u>God's Search for Man: a Philosophy of Judaism</u> (NY: Farrar, Straus, Giroux, 1955), 4 and Isaiah 40:26, quoted in Heschel, 33
28. Genesis 1:1-2.

the Sabbath.[29] As captives in Babylon, they had no temple in which to pray and offer animal sacrifices, a substitute for human sacrifice. In this situation they turned to what they had, the writings of their ancestors, especially those ascribed to Moses and the prophets. The prophets had announced that exile would be punishment for the sins of the nation and that the restoration to their homeland would be evidence of God's fidelity. Their collection of psalms was a kind of prayerbook and became itself a source of prophetic pronouncements reinforcing faith in God's fidelity to a people even amidst their infidelity.

On the Sabbath, even in their situation as exiles, they could prayerfully contemplate the scriptures which called them to rest with the creator, and at rest they intuited the wholeness or oneness of creation in an I-Thou relationship with the Creator. The first story of creation in Genesis is a worship hymn which celebrates this intuition. It begins with God saying, "Let there be light, and there was light" and its refrain is "God saw it was good."[30] The text seems to be an observation of a single day dawning, night giving way to light, light separating out from darkness. To worship at dawn is to see things afresh, every day is potentially a new creation. Morning breaks like the first morning. No wonder God saw it was good. But there is more. Having waited in darkness there is an intuition that even before creation, when there is only darkness, there is nevertheless something that is good. Even before the light begins to separate from the darkness, there is God, Goodness itself. Both the darkness and the light, and by extension all that follows, share in the goodness that is meant by naming God as creator. The Jewish myth of creation declares that everything in the universe, whether darkness or light, reflects the Goodness who is the creator.

---

29. It was during their exile in Babylon while absent the Jerusalem Temple and its rituals sacrifices that the Jewish community formed the synagogue (gathering) in which the written Law became the defining character of Jewish worship and life.
30. Genesis 1:3.

The first day of creation, "God saw how good the light was. God then separated the light from the darkness. God called the light 'day,' and the darkness he called 'night.' Thus evening came, and morning followed - the first day."[31] Here is the beginning some would say of duality, night and day, darkness and light. It seems more accurate to say here is the beginning of equality, defined as each thing having its own reality, its own share in goodness, and yet only by being interrelated can anything find its wholeness.[32] Only together are light and darkness the first day, night followed by morning. This perspective on equality, not sameness but difference as source of wholeness, will be immensely important in understanding both the creation of male and female as one humanity and the place of humankind among the many life-forms on Earth.

In the first chapter of Genesis, the one God of the Jews is called El (God). El is whom Jesus called Abba, or Father. But in Christian theology there is an evolved understanding of the oneness of God. While God remains the only God, and in that sense the one God, God's oneness for Christians is as a Trinitarian communion. The Jews understood both the Word and Spirit to be expressions of El's power and intention. Thomas Aquinas (1224-1274), Dominican priest and theologian, explained that according to the Christian faith Spirit and Word are equal to the Father in power and majesty and go forth into the mission of salvation in such unity as to be "equal from

---

31. Genesis 1:4-5.
32. The word "equality" can be defined in logical or conceptual reasoning as "same," as in we are all equal before the law. With situational thinking, equality makes room for "difference," as Paul does in First Corinthians 12 where he speaks of each part of the body being different but being equally necessary to the unity of a physical body or a relational community. Equality before the law is dependent on our recognition of a person's equality in our relational community (our human situation); this equality is what we call "human dignity." On Earth, while not every creature has equal standing before human law, every creature, precisely because of difference, is equally integral to an environmental system.

51

equal."[33] Creation is the beginning of the mission of salvation, of bringing to fulfillment the plan of God for the material creation. Therefore, in Christian theology God's spirit moving over the void in preparation for creation and God's word spoken as the act of creation can be interpreted as the work of the Trinity, One God. Creation is the beginning of a divine mission that is yet to be fulfilled in the Cosmos, a mission to bring all things into a divine relational way of being.

Now let us consider the second day of creation which repurposes the myth of Tiamat's body providing the boundary between Earth and the waters. "Then God said, 'Let there be a dome in the middle of the waters, to separate one body of water from the other.' And so it happened: God made the dome, and it separated the water above the dome from the water below it. God called the dome 'the sky.' Evening came, and morning followed - the second day."[34] God divides the waters above and below the sky but absent any sacrificial victim. However, this dome above called sky and Earth below are much like my third-grade art piece. The picture gives the impression that Earth is flat and floating on water, and we live in the space between sky and Earth. Our perspective on Earth and sky have radically evolved over the last several centuries.

On the third day, God separates water from land, names each, and then calls forth the plants, trees, fruits, and seeds in the watered landscape.[35] Notice how each day God gives names to what is created. Naming is a divine power, since a name gives a place to each thing in its relationship with the rest, as we see clearly on the fourth day. Even the heavenly bodies and time itself are given place and purpose in God's creation. On the fourth day, the lights of the heavens appear together; sun, moon, and stars, a moment of

33. Catherine Mowry LaCugna, God for Us: the Trinity and Christian life (San Francisco: Harper, 1991), 157.
34. Genesis 1:6-8.
35. Genesis 1:9-12.

extraordinary beauty, the heavenly lights hung together in the sky. "Then God said: 'Let there be lights in the dome of the sky, to separate day from night. Let them mark the fixed times, the days and the years, and serve as luminaries in the dome of the sky, to shed light upon the earth'."[36] With lights in the sky that circle Earth the human observer would easily perceive that Earth is the steady center of the Cosmos.

Once again, however, the Jewish perspective differentiates these lights from the myths of surrounding peoples which speak of them as gods to be worshipped. No, they are lights provided by the creator, fellow creatures who function as a cosmic clock identifying times and seasons. Genesis makes it clear that nothing in creation is worthy of worship, only God who created all things. Yet each thing has its own dignity as it reflects the goodness of the creator. The compassionate creator even makes time a companion to humankind and not our taskmaster or "god."

Companioned by time, the text next offers a prescient possibility for the evolution of species on Earth. The text predates Darwin's research by at least two and a half millennia. As it unfolds on the fifth and sixth days, the creation of the diverse species fills sea, sky, and land. But life begins in the waters and then comes forth on the dry land. God sees how good all of this is. Formed in response to the word of the creator, they are neither powers to be emulated nor gods to be worshiped, but fellow creatures. As theologian John Haught, who directed the Georgetown Center for Science and Religion, wrote in God after Darwin, "Nature, when understood as essentially promise [not completion], would have intrinsic, but by no means ultimate, value."[37] It is not creation but creation's God who is the ultimate value to whom creation is being drawn for its fulfillment.

---

36. Genesis 1:14-15.
37. John Haught, God after Darwin: A theology of evolution (Boulder, CO: Westview Press, 2000), 157.

Some Christians, unlike the Jewish editors of Genesis, take a fundamentalist approach to the creation myth. They do so to uphold the sovereignty of God over creation. However, this means that even in the face of the scientific evidence of evolution, they interpret the days of creation analytically, establishing a pseudo-scientific explanation of the mechanics of creation. That approach equates each of the six days of creation with a twenty-four-hour Earth-day and declares the Cosmos began less than six thousand years ago. Perhaps those who want to take this analytical approach do not recognize the prayerfulness and poetry of these verses which provide the reader with an intuition of creation's true relationship with God.

Some religious persons have refused to accept the literary and historical research which shows that Genesis is not meant to substitute for a modern scientific version of creation. Many, especially among Christians who maintain a literal, analytical interpretation of Genesis, also maintain that original sin corrupted the goodness of the whole of creation, and especially the whole of our humanity. Is it true, the goodness of creation was only in the beginning and is now past because of sin? That is an apocalyptic view of creation's current state, which in turn condemns the material world, believing it to be an idol which needs to be destroyed in order to accelerate the end of time and the restoration of God's original intent.[38]

Instead, taking our perspective from its Sabbath conclusion on the seventh day, the story of creation is about what God creates, sustains, and will bring to fulfillment through an I-Thou relationship, a relationship which remains because it is initiated by God. Genesis makes clear that creation is an act of self-revelation by the Creator, an act of outpouring of shared being. What God calls into being and calls good remains good, including human nature. We will continue

38. Antonio Sparado, "Reflections on 'Fratelli Tuti'," La Civilta Cattolica, October 8, 2020.

in chapter three with our consideration of the creation of humankind on the sixth day.

Conclusion

In these first two chapters, we have considered how scientific and theological research interact from their differing perspectives and are able to inform each other about the beginnings of the Cosmos. The material sciences ask what a thing is and what are the causes for its being what it is. Textual research asks the meanings of a text and its original sources and how these meanings change in differing contexts. Theology asks why a thing is what it is and what its relationship is with other things, especially the creator. In the next two chapters, we will examine more closely the possibility of cooperation between these differing perspectives for our understanding of the human species and of its responsibility for the preservation of Earth and the life Earth has brought forth and sustains.

Chapter III

Homo Sapiens

The Evolution of Our Species

Contemporary sciences offer us important information about the evolution of the Cosmos and of our human race. The Big Bang occurred about 13.8 billion years ago. Life on Earth began 4.2 billion years ago, and our primate ancestors 15 million years ago. We have many ancestors among even more ancient life-forms than primates, as is evident from pictures during the first eight weeks of our embryonic development.

Africa is the historic womb for the origin of our genus *Homo*, Latin for humans. While our genus has common hominid ancestors with apes and chimpanzees, we became a separate genus around 2.5 million years ago. Over the subsequent millennia, there evolved perhaps more than two dozen of our genus or hominin ancestors. None of them currently exist, but some of their DNA is present in our species today. As recently as June 2021, Science News reported another species was found in Israel which may have contributed to our DNA.[39]

There are points of intersection between this scientific data and the story of the creation of the world as presented in the Book of Genesis. For instance, Genesis speaks of Eve as "the mother of all the living," and contemporary genomic research shows all humans

---

39. Bruce Bower, "Israeli fossil finds reveal a new hominid group, Nesher Ramla Homo," Science News, June 24, 2021. https://www.sciencenews.org /article/israel-fossil-new-hominid-nesher-ramla-homo-human-evolution, accessed July 30, 2021. Previous contributors to the gene pool of *Homo sapiens*, as recently as 40 to 14 thousand years ago, include Neanderthals who inhabited present day Europe and areas of northern Asia and Denisovans from the Middle East and parts of Asia. Anthropologists differ on the evolution of the only remaining hominin species, *Homo sapiens*, but it ranges from 300,000 to 200,000 years ago.

currently living on Earth can be traced to a single original mother. [40] That ancestor lived relatively recently in evolutionary time, a mere 200,000 years ago. We also have evidence of a Y-Chromosomal Adam from about the same period as Mitochondrial Eve. This kind of information can inspire more scientific curiosity about *how* we are part of the whole of life on Earth. However, the stories told in Genesis about *why* our human race is part of creation are more likely to motivate us to act for the sake of the whole of us on Earth. The scientific data shows we are interdependent with other creatures. The ancient stories in Genesis can motivate us to preserve that interdependence as the balance needed to sustain life on Earth.

The action necessary for the preservation of life on Earth was described by Thomas Berry four decades ago. "Our challenge is to create a new language, even a new sense of what it is to be human. It is to transcend not only national limitations, but even our species isolation, to enter into the larger community of living species. This brings about a completely new sense of reality and value."[41] The old language of species privilege allowed us to dominate other creatures. We *Homo sapiens*, or "wise humans," need a new language if we are to sustain our relationships with each other and the other life-forms on Earth. The Genesis myths of the creation of humans offer a foundation for that new language.

Humanity's Place in Creation

The myth of creation in the first chapter of Genesis is told in the style of a hymn used in worship of God. The refrain of the hymn is the creator's repeated declaration that creation is good. This hymn of creation inspired Francis of Assisi (1181-1220) to pen his famous poem, "The Canticle of Brother Sun." In it, he praised God for the

---

40. Cann RL, Stoneking M, Wilson AC., Cann, R. L. "Mitochondrial DNA and human evolution" in Nature (1987, Jan) 1-7.
41. Thomas Berry, "The Ecological Age," in The Dream of the Earth, Berkeley: Counterpoint Press, 2015 (orig. San Francisco: Sierra Club Books, 1988), 42.

goodness of each creature in nature. Why is everything in creation good? Because God is Good, and each creature God creates reflects the Goodness of the creator. That means goodness is the formal cause of creation. Goodness is the form given to each creature. For that reason, every creature remains good despite our experience to the contrary. That is not the way most of us think about things. Nevertheless, that is the truth contained in the first Genesis myth, the creator made and sustains everything in the goodness that is God's way of being.

Each creature simply by existing is an expression of the goodness of the creator; each thing exists as its own self and cannot exist other than having its own existence. As the Jesuit priest and poet Gerard Manley Hopkins observed in his poem *Kingfishers*, "Each mortal thing does one thing and the same: Deals out that being indoors each one dwells; Selves—goes itself; myself it speaks and spells."[42] Each tangible thing is unique in its way of being, which is what being is all about. Nothing is unless it is as itself. Each part of creation is unique in its relationship to the creator.

For humans, the first gift God gives is existence as his or her own self. Each human exists as his or her unique self, even scientifically down to the chromosomal level which physically marks our differentiation. Furthermore, our ability to reflect on ourselves allows each of us to make a unique response through our personal relationships with the creator and each other. It is the quality of our responses which brings us from the image to the likeness of God. Image and likeness obviously do not mean looking like God, as if we

---

42. Gerard Manley Hopkins, S.J. wrote the sonnet "As Kingfishers Catch Fire" around 1882 but the poem was not published until 1918, almost 30 years after his death from typhoid in 1889. His reputation as a poet grew in the 1920s, and a second publication of his works by Charles Williams in 1930 began the wider distribution of his poems. Given the history of the writing and distribution of his poems, it is evident that his poems make Hopkins an integral literary companion of the evolution of contemporary cosmology with its sense of the inwardness of nature.

are genetically God's children, or having equality in the kind of existence that belongs to God alone. We are always created beings. Instead, it is our response to God, to each creature, and to Earth itself that manifests God's image and likeness in us. Our responses affirm or contradict the image of God who cares for and shepherds to fulfillment all that is.

Here recall what Rabbi Heschel said about the three starting points of contemplation about God, worship, learning, and action. Like the hymn that is the story of creation all worship begins with "Lift up your eyes and see who created these."[43] It is among concrete things that we live, and move, and find life. Seeing the goodness of each created thing and the beauty manifest in the interrelationship, their wholeness as one creation, we are moved to worship the creator-God. Learning more about God is also best done by thinking about what is particular and concrete in the work of God. Through that kind of situational thinking we learn about God's purpose for humans and the actions God invites us to undertake to sustain life on Earth. For instance, the first story of creation contextualizes the creation of humankind on the same day as the other animals. Science shows that we evolved from these other life-forms. Both Genesis and science show that humans are fellow creatures with other animals, but Genesis states that the concrete difference is the work given to humans by the creator.

On the sixth day humankind is given life and on that same day given specific work to do. The work continues to unfold in the historical circumstances of humanity. The work we are given is our unique way of being-related to Earth and its creatures, and it reflects one of the ways we are in the image of God. Humankind comes into existence as self-reflective beings able to care about creation. For this reason, God gives humankind "dominion over the fish of the sea, the birds of the air, and all the living things that move on the Earth."[44]

---

43. Heschel, 31.
44. Genesis 1:28.

The gift of dominion over Earth and its creatures was interpreted in seventeenth century Europe in a conceptual, rather than a situational way. Dominion was logically interpreted as the power to dominate. Humans had the God-given right to turn Earth into a free market in which to make whatever profit one desired. [45] That interpretation created the language of species privilege, the rationale for the misuse of Earth and its creatures over the succeeding five centuries. The interpretation of dominion as "domination" could well continue to control the use of the solar system through interplanetary travel when that becomes possible. That is unless a better interpretation of Genesis or the establishment of some similar myth finds place among us and soon.

The truth contained in the Genesis myths is that humans are to sustain creation's interrelatedness and thus promote synergy, our collaborative working together with the rest of nature. These God-given responsibilities of humans are rooted in our relational way of being. Theologically, we understand that our interrelatedness is the way that God created us. It is an essential dimension of the form of goodness, of being in the divine image. Scientifically, we understand our interrelatedness is rooted in the fact that our species evolved from the very life-forms from which all the other forms of life on Earth evolved. Both Genesis and science show it is these life-forms for whom we are to care. St. Francis of Assisi famously called them brothers and sisters, as have many ancient peoples, including First Nation Americans. The Genesis story presents that relational way of

---

45. The reference in the text is to Adam Smith (1723-1790, Edinburgh) a political economist whose writings on capitalism were the economic counterpart to political absolutism. Like-minded Europeans were Jean-Baptiste Colbert in France and Antonio Serra in Italy. Also, David Hume (1711-1776) who was a Scottish Enlightenment philosopher whose writing reflected empiricism, skepticism, and naturalism, while rejecting the objectivity of religious experiences. Hume supported a scientific parallel to capitalism and political absolutism, which was insistence on the perfectibility of the world through scientific observation and testing.

being as the situation in which human "dominion" is to be understood.

In Genesis 1:28, God blesses the man and woman saying, "Be fertile and multiply; fill the earth and subdue it. Have dominion over the fish of the sea, the birds of the air, and all the living things that move on the earth." The original Hebrew text used two verbs, *kavash* for subdue and *radah* for have dominion. *Kavash* implies other creatures will be the subjects of humankind, but *radah* gives special nuance to this subject-status. *Radah* does not mean to lord it over a subject but to administer benevolent care toward a subject. It is not by being a dictator or by conquering but by benevolent leadership, being among other creatures as one of them, that humankind is to tend creation. Here is the image of the Creator in which humankind is made. God's workplan thus clarifies humankind's relationship with other creatures, with the environment, and with God. Humankind will be provided for by and in turn will learn from the rest of creation how to care for it as God cares for all.

Additional evidence for the care humans are to give other creatures is God's gift of food. For God also said: "See, I give you every seed-bearing plant on all the Earth and every tree that has seed-bearing fruit on it to be your food; and to all the wild animals, all the birds of the air, and all the living creatures that crawl on the Earth, I give all the green plants for food. And so it happened."[46] There is no need in this first myth of creation for the random sacrifice of the life of another, even among animals, to sustain the life of any creature.[47]

---

46. Genesis 1:29-30.
47. Vegetarianism is implied by this verse, as a feature of the peaceful interrelatedness of all creation at its beginning. The passage suggests that without putting any sentient life form to death for food, there was still abundance of life on Earth at the beginning. It is this idyllic state Isaiah promises is the work of God in the future (Isaiah 11:6-9), and Christians believe Christ will accomplish it at his second coming by bringing about the fullness of the Kingdom of God. In Genesis, other sentient creatures are first given for human food only after Noah successfully saves them from the flood that ravished all life-forms (Genesis 9:3-5).

It is to this whole work of creation the response is given, "God looked at everything made, and found it very good. Evening came and morning followed, the sixth day."[48]

The absence of killing in this first story of creation, even of one creature eating the flesh of another, seems idyllic.[49] It gave rise to the belief that in the beginning there was no violence or death, even for the sake of nourishment, only peaceful coexistence. Why was the story told that way? It is a literary device called a prolepsis. That peaceful coexistence of all sentient life-forms on the sixth day epitomizes beforehand the fulfillment of creation promised on the seventh day. The fulfillment of creation is Sabbath rest, resting with God. In a similar way, the prophet Isaiah described the peace that would ensue when the promised age of Emmanuel, "God with us," would unfold. The lion would lie down with the lamb and a child could play at a cobra's den.[50]

While it is a law among the Jewish people that they rest from work on the seventh day each week, the Sabbath rest is more than an imitation of God having finished the work of creation. God continues to sustain creation and draw it to its completion. That is why the people are to renew their life by resting with God who rests in the whole of what God has made. This rest is joining in a contemplative way of being, resting one in the other. God in creation, creation in God. This is the fulfillment to which we and all creation are called, and to which humans are to lead the whole. Just so, we pray for our deceased that they may rest in divine peace with no more

---

48. Genesis 1:31.
49. It is not until chapter nine in Genesis when Noah and all the animals exit the Ark after the great flood that God gives permission to eat the meat of animals. Meat with blood remaining in it, however, is not to be eaten. Blood stands for the essence of life which belongs in God's care. Neither is anyone, animal or human, to kill a human being. Any shedding of the blood of a human requires that the one who shed it, animal or human, be put to death. The reason for this prohibition and consequence is that humans are in the image of God, as caretakers of all the creatures, as the story of the Ark emphasized.
50. Isaiah 11:1-12.

tears, sadness, violence, or death. However, according to Maximus the Confessor (580-662 C.E.), a Byzantine monk, theologian and scholar, this rest is not a static state of perfection but an eternal adventure of discovery in the wonder of being alive in God forever.

What else can we discern from the creation of humans in the image of God? God said: "Let us make human beings in our image, after our likeness. Let them have dominion over the fish of the sea, the birds of the air, the tame animals, all the wild animals, and all the creatures that crawl on the Earth. God created humankind in [the divine] image; in God's image they were created; male and female God created them."[51] Notice, humankind's creation in the image of God is defined in terms of the care of creation from their position as creatures among other creatures. Human beings exist not aside from but as a part of nature. The work we are to do is described as dominion whose Latin root *domus* means home. Earth is a home where humankind is to oversee the care of all the members of the household. The Hebrew root for oversee is once again, *radah*, benevolent care. Presumably, leadership of other creatures in the way of benevolence begins with leadership of ourselves.

From the context one may conclude that the relationship between male and female must also be that same one of care. However, when sexual difference is reduced to genital difference, it is easier to seek domination, one over the other. Although mutual benevolent care of each sex with the other (and not dictatorship of any kind) is suggested by the context, it has not been the norm in human relationships any more than has been our benevolent care of other creatures. In fact, the first creation myth does not deal with the complexity of human sexual relationships. It simply establishes that there is one humanity created as two sexes, male and female, and that their creation is in the image of God. In this myth, the image of God is the care of all life

---

51. Genesis 1:27-28.

that God has created on Earth. But that clearly implies the benevolent care of each other in our sexual differentiation.

Religion and Science on Sex

Each society judges human sexual expression according to its unique operative cultural myth. In the twentieth century, there were changes in the mythic understanding of western cultures concerning homosexual expressions. These changes occurred because of historical, cultural, psychological, and neuroscientific inquiry into human sexuality. Homosexuality appears across human history and in all cultures and societies. In the latter half of the twentieth century, western psychology changed from declaring homosexuality a mental disease to calling it a human variant. That change was primarily driven by social and historical reasons, but is there scientific evidence for this new perspective on homosexuality as a human variant?

Neuroscience is succeeding in explaining the development of the human brain and its complex operation regarding sexual preference. Still, theological claims about human sexuality among various Christian churches remain centered primarily on three issues: 1) the moral use of human sexual organs, 2) the social and spiritual purposes of sexual intercourse, and 3) heterosexual parenting as the environment proper for the rearing of children. These theological assertions describe human sexuality in terms of the complementarity of sexual organs for the birth of children. They declare this physical sexual complementary a feature of natural law, along with the different patterns of parenting by males and females on which child development depends. Thus, these claims assert only the moral goodness of heterosexual relationships.

These theological claims hold that among humans, sexual intercourse has two natural purposes, to foster unity in the couple's relationship and to beget children. They state that the sexual unity between heterosexual partners in marriage is the only moral foundation for the begetting and rearing of children.

Of course, when a woman suffers from a lack of benevolent care in a heterosexual relationship, the unity of persons is violated, but the woman still may bear a child in that relationship. In such instances, the lack of benevolent care has a profound deleterious effect on all three persons and on the society in which this violation occurs. It is also true that those who seek homosexual relationships have suffered even greater violation of the creator's intent of benevolent care for all persons. Does society benefit from this violation of benevolent care? The Catholic Church has officially called for persons who experience homosexual attraction to be treated with benevolence but continues to teach that their sexual desires are not oriented to the divinely created purposes of human sexual expression.

If the dialogue between science and theology is to bear fruit in the benevolent care of humans, of both males and females, we must address the question science poses about homosexuality. As James Alison states, "[It] is fairly simple: either it is true that being gay or lesbian is a vicious or pathological form of a humanity which is only authentically heterosexual; or it is true that being gay and lesbian is simply something that is a non-pathological minority variant in the human condition."[52] If the latter, "the appropriate humanization of sexual desire will be worked out in appropriate relationships over time."[53] It is my opinion that this humanization would require us to understand that the templates for arousal, attraction and attachment are part of the natural order of human sexuality.

In my training as a sexual addiction therapist, I learned that sexual desire depends upon three templates in the organic structure of the human brain. A template is a model for the brain to follow in performing some task. A template is part of the organic structure of the brain. That means a template is in place in the material that makes

---

52. James Allison, The Guardian, October 22, 2020.
https://www.theguardian.com/commentisfree/2020/oct/22/pope-francis-same-sex-unions-surprise-gay-people, accessed June 20, 2021.
53. Ibid.

up the brain, nerves, and synapses (connections), prior to any decision to act on the model the template offers.

Each person has three templates that are part of the structure of the brain. These templates are the models for what will sexually arouse, attract, and motivate a person to attach with another. These three templates 1) initiate the arousal of sexual feelings and physical responses, 2) inspire a person's attraction to another person, or sexual attention, and 3) draw us to attach to another person in an ongoing, even permanent, relationship.

These templates work independently of each other and prior to any decision to act out our sexual desire. They model for us our own responses to another person's various traits, whether intellectual, physical, emotional, social, financial, or spiritual. When all three templates center on a person of the same sex, it is generally accepted to be an indication a person is homosexual in orientation. If on the opposite sex, the person is heterosexual.

Of course, human arousal, attraction and attachment are on a spectrum between male and female and not simply one or the other. Our templates create a spectrum of sexual interest toward persons of the opposite sex or same sex. That means we can be more or less responsive to both sexes, just as we can be strongly responsive to one sex or the other. However, when an individual's templates orient more clearly to the same or the opposite sex, that person is said to have an orientation, either homosexual or heterosexual.

The templates which control our sexual desire are believed to be set prior to seven years of age, the age of reason and rationally informed choice. There is some indication that during gestation in the womb, genes that affect these templates are turned on or off. So far, science seems to support the belief that same-sex orientation is a variant in the human condition. However, even though homosexuality occurs across history and cultures, we still await definitive empirical evidence that homosexuality is in fact a non-pathological minority variant in the human condition.

The question is what kind of evidence will suffice. Would a gay gene be sufficient to overcome millennia of religious objection? Meanwhile, calling a person's sexual templates contrary to nature excludes that person's inclinations for sexual arousal, attraction, and attachment from the natural order of creation and declares that a person's templates are contrary to the intent of the creator. This, even though these templates are not put in place by a personal rational decision but by natural processes.

The context for the creation of humans in Genesis is heterosexual relations. This is so because such relationships were necessary for the cohesion of the Jewish people and for their continuation. A person is born a Jew into a covenantal relationship with God. Because the Genesis myths only include heterosexual relations, benevolent care has not been extended to same-sex relationships by cultures based on interpretations of Judeo-Christian scriptures. Among these cultures, intercourse between persons of the same sex is frequently considered contrary to nature because such intercourse lacks the sexual complementarity capable of begetting children. This is true even though some persons in same-sex relationships have created stable intentional families. Nevertheless, persons who desire to attach with someone of the same sex continue to be treated in many societies as abnormal or even as outlaws, despite the fact their same-sexual attachment has created unity between them as persons and fostered stable relationships.[54]

---

54. It is beyond the scope of this chapter to clarify issues of gender identity or medically induced sex change which are issues currently being debated particularly in the western culture. Pope Francis has been firm in his negative responses in these debates. However, among many of our fellow creatures homosexual expression and even changes in sexual identity are not rare. Mammalian homosexual expression and sex change among amphibians, as well as many varieties of fish, come to mind. The Jewish scriptures condemn bestiality and cross-dressing among humans, while texts in both Jewish and Christian scriptures condemn homosexual acts as immoral. Historically, benevolent care was not extended to homosexuals in societies based on these Judeo-Christian writings. The result has been to exclude any possibility of a spectrum in natural

Francis stepped into this conversation before he became Pope. As Archbishop of Buenos Aries, he supported civil unions for gays. In doing so, he offered a context for situational thinking. The context in which humans live is more contingent, more diverse than logical assertions allow. As such, the Archbishop went beyond an argument about sexual acts being able to both create unity and conceive children. He began a discussion of the anthropological need of every human for family relationships. What he did not do is equate civil unions with sacramental marriage between a male and a female, which is the context for begetting children and sexually creating families. Nevertheless, Pope Francis has continued to insist that gay persons need families and should not be excluded from partaking in family life.

It is in the interest of societies to support family life. Homosexual intercourse can and has functioned to unite persons committed to developing family life that includes children from previous heterosexual relationships, adoptions, extended family members, and the marginalized in society. Some civil governments have reasoned that it should be possible, therefore, based on the human need for family, that civil recognition be given persons who stabilize their family life in a same-sex relationship. This approach to family life allows synergy and interrelationship, which are the unitive purpose of sexual acts, to find their crown in intentional family life, which is not limited to the procreation and human formation of one's biological children. This form of recognition would be part of the appropriate humanization of same-sexual desire over time, at least as far as some civil societies view the matter.

---

sexual differentiation and to hold there are only two sexes and these are naturally attracted only to their opposites. This interpretation of human sexual differentiation in turn has supported civil and religious societal condemnation both of same-sex relationships and of current sexual identity theories.

Societies continue to draw diverse conclusions based on their diverse operative myths.[55] These myths are used, both consciously and often unconsciously, to interpret historical, cultural, and scientific data. The result is that in many western countries same-sex unions have gained civil recognition, while in other countries, persons are still liable to the death penalty for such relationships. The morality of homosexual relationships, in which the unitive function of sex is separated from its biological function of procreation, remains a heavily debated issue in theologically informed discussions, even as international societal and legal responses remain vastly divergent.[56]

Conclusion

In this chapter, we noted that science looks at how life, including human life, came about on Earth. Science finds that all life emerged as interrelated, creating a whole in which all the parts participate according to their own kind. The theological foundation for Christianity's understanding of life on Earth is found in the Jewish scriptures. The Book of Genesis (Beginnings) also describes the wholeness of creation and its interrelatedness by emphasizing the why of creation. Creation is created good in the image of God who is goodness itself. Genesis also expresses the belief that human life

---

55. Some societal myths hold that sex, gender, and identity are assigned by nature. For instance, some hold that heterosexuality and homosexuality are not a choice a person makes but assigned by nature and, therefore nature's creator. Still other myths hold that a person's identity is chosen based on that person's self-understanding. For instance, a person chooses to be homosexual and can change the choice. Others hold all gender identity is chosen based on self-understanding, but these theories do not assign an age of reason or a time in life when self-understanding of this sort is complete.

56. An example of this debate is Margaret Farely, R.S.M., Just Love: a Framework for Christian Sexual Ethics, (NY: Continuum International Publishing Group, 2006). Dr. Farely is a Catholic religious sister and Gilbert L. Stark Professor Emerita of Christian Ethics at the Yale Divinity School. She reframes ethical issues in terms of the relational nature of human existence.

was created to care for creation, as the creator continues to do, and to accompany creation to its fulfillment and ours. Fulfillment is described as rest, that fulness of peace of our interrelatedness which is yet to come but which can be tasted in this creation.

In this chapter, we also pointed out that Genesis describes the dominion of humankind over Earth and its creatures as caring for all the members of the household to which we belong. The work the creator gave to us is to be among the other creatures as the caregiver to each other and all of life's forms. The Genesis myth was reinterpreted by western Enlightenment thinkers, beginning in the 1600s. The Enlightenment's interpretation used science as a tool for domination of Earth, through the mechanized use of creation for the furtherance of human consumption. At the same time, Christians in western nations supported that modern mythic interpretation of our role on Earth by promoting economic and political systems of domination of persons and of the gifts of Earth, all of which are vital to sustaining life. The tendency to dominate was expressed in multiple ways, including colonialism, racism, sexism, and species privilege.

At the end of this chapter, we introduced the question that science in the post-modern age poses about homosexuality. Science is conducting an ongoing inquiry into empirical evidence concerning human sexuality. In the historical evolution of *Homo sapiens* is sexual expression limited by physical genital complementarity, male and female? If so, what then do we make of the continuous historical occurrence of homosexuality across cultures? Based on the first creation account in Genesis, we were created male and female, and Jewish law proscribed same sex acts. Christians have traditionally done the same.

The dialogue between science and religion has resulted in some Christian communities accepting homosexual relationships and others not. Among Catholics this dialogue has resulted in official teaching that persons with same-sex attractions are, nonetheless, to be treated with human dignity and remain members of the Catholic Church. At the same time, their inclination to homosexual relationships is said to be disordered from the creator's purpose of human sexual acts. The question is whether the dialogue between science and theology will bring about further developments in this dimension of human self-understanding. If it does, it might well be the result of a deeper understanding of the human capacity for intimacy as presented in the second creation myth in Genesis.

Chapter IV

A Second Creation Myth

Male and Female

The two creation myths in the Book of Genesis are the foundation of Judeo-Christian anthropology, what it means to be human from a theological perspective. The second story of creation further develops the Jewish mythic understanding of humanity's relational way of being. The first story of creation in Genesis is cosmic and uses a generic name for the Creator-God (El or Elohim). The second story uses the personal name for God. This name is so sacred to the Jewish people that it is not pronounced by them nor written here.[57] The name is translated into English as "I Am" and inaugurates creation into a relational way of being, as "Thou."

The second myth especially highlights the relational way of being that is human life. It does so by centering on human relationships first with the creator, then with Earth and other animals, and finally between male and female as generators of human life. As such, the second myth of creation is highly contextual. It is not a hymn like the first, but more like the way a potter would explain her relationship to water and clay, or a farmer his relationship to the land, his mate, and his God.

---

57. The divine name is written as a Tetragram, in English letters YHWH. It is composed of four letters from the Hebrew alphabet which are only written after praying and never pronounced because the name is too sacred. Instead, the Tetragram is read as "Lord," or *Adoni* in Hebrew, and often accompanied by "my" or "the." Because there was confusion over this practice of substituting another name to be pronounced instead of the Tetragram, the letters of the two words which compose *Adoni* and the Tetragram were thought to be single word, which some in recent centuries spelled out as "Jehovah," a name for God that is not present in ancient Hebrew, Greek, or Latin editions of the Bible.

The second myth begins with the same necessary ambiguity as the first, "*When* God made the Earth and the heavens."[58] The word *when* sounds like time in English. But to the Greek mind, which influenced early Christianity, it appeared as an intentional act of going out of self, called *ekstasis*. The way the creator exists is to pour out existence, so in Christian thought *when* is the dynamic outpouring of God in sharing existence with creatures. The time involved is not chronological (*Kronos* in Greek), but a time of fulfillment (*Kairos*). It is an event in which only a creator could provide the formal and final causes for a material universe (the reason for creation and what ultimately it will be). Therefore, this myth gives first place to the creation of Earth, because it is through life on Earth that humans will come to know the creator. As we will see in the following chapter, when humankind evolves the capacity for religious thinking, nature itself will reveal God to the human consciousness.

The second myth of creation begins with Earth and leads to the creation of the mother of later generations of humans, Eve. Between Mother Earth and Mother Eve, Adam is created.[59] Adam stands for all humans. Adam is the corporate person of humankind, what is known in philosophy as a universal particular. Only with the creation of Eve does humankind achieve sexual differentiation.

As this divine creative act begins, there is already soil and water which bubbles up as a spring.[60] It is a scene reminiscent of a potter's workplace set with water and clay. Having mixed these as a potter would, the creator fashions Adam. *Adamah* is Hebrew for the red soil of the region from which the name Adam is derived. Similarly, the name *human* in English comes from *humus*, the word for soil. Adam later will remain the proper name for the first human to till the soil. But there is much more afoot.

---

58. Genesis 2:4.
59. *Gaea* in ancient Greek is the primordial mother and her name was used for Earth.
60. Genesis 2:5-7.

"Then the Lord God formed the man out of the dust of the ground and blew into his nostrils the breath of life, and the man became a living being."[61] This action shows how unique the relationship is between the God of the Jews and all humanity. God personally blows into the nostrils of Adam the breath of life and Adam becomes a living being. Here is a claim to something unique about humanity. Human persons share a unique way of being alive; they have in them a breath or spirit that is a sharing in God. Some may want to say every life form has the breath of God in it. Others will say it shows humans did not evolve from prior species because Genesis says only Adam directly received the breath of God. The Jewish editors have a different interest.

Adam stands for all human beings. Through the human capacity for self-reflection and choice, Adam is to come to know God and make a direct and personal response to God. This is an intimate relationship the other animals do not share in the same way. It is toward this potentially direct, full, and conscious relationship with God that all human beings are brought forth into life. It is toward the fulfillment of this relationship that God mentors and sustains the strivings of our human race.

God next creates Eden to be the place where the human may live. A similar-sounding Hebrew word means pleasure park. Eden is Earth with all its possibilities. Eden also is suggestive of the promised land, known as a land flowing with milk and honey, into which God through Moses guided the Jewish people. The Jewish editors of Genesis were exiled from that promised land like Adam and Eve will be from Eden.

The next creative act of God is to create the animals from the ground, that is from Earth, as companions for Adam who is given a divine power, naming the animals.[62] In ancient wisdom cultures,

---

61. Genesis 2:7.
62. Genesis 2:18-20.

naming is knowing; a name is not just a label but the story of a creature's interrelatedness with self and others. To name the animals is to create a relationship, to tell a story of association. This is true of the name Adam, which associates all humankind with the soil from which they came, and so with the Earth from which they evolved, and with the Cosmos from which the Earth evolved. We have the same origin as all the other life-forms on Earth. Modern humans even call themselves Earthlings, especially as they anticipate traveling into the Cosmos.

In creating the animals, the creator is sensitive to Adam's need for companionship, but they prove unsuitable partners.[63] Knowing that an association with other creatures is not the same as having another like oneself, God creates from Adam's own rib, next to Adam's heart, another human being. The word "sex" comes from *secare* which is Latin for "to divide or cut." It is this sexual difference, when finally expressed in the story, that marks the differentiation in Adam, the corporate human person, into male and female. Whereas the first myth in Genesis emphasized the unity of one humankind created as male and female, this second story emphasizes that the sexual difference between male and female will be the source of unity between them in forming one humanity.

Adam says, "This one, at last, is bone of my bones and flesh of my flesh; this one shall be called 'woman,' for out of man this one has been taken."[64] And the narrator adds, "That is why a man leaves his father and mother and clings to his wife, and the two of them become one body. The man and his wife were both naked, yet they felt no shame."[65] The sexual differentiation of Adam and Eve establishes their tangible existence as male and female and makes available their partnership in a relationship as husband and wife. Here

---

63. Genesis 2:20-22.
64. Genesis 2:23.
65. Genesis 2:24-25.

is the basis for theological claims about the complementarity between the sexes being part of the law of God written into nature. The theological claim is that sexual union is designed by the creator solely for the purpose of marriage between one man and one woman who in turn may have potential for becoming parents.

From the perspective of modern science, God's command in Genesis for Adam and Eve to multiply and fill Earth was written into our brains and hormonal systems as we evolved from other mammalian life. That is why sexuality has a great deal of compulsion about it. To put it in common language, if sex was not such a compulsion for us there would probably never be babies. Part of human sexuality, however, is initiated by the neurological templates discussed in the previous chapter. These templates are empirical evidence that sexual arousal, attraction, and attachment are constructed through natural brain development prior to the age of reason.

In Western Christianity, theological assertions about human behavior, or moral theology, have relied heavily on a stoic view of the universe as rational. This approach has much in common with modern science. Both emphasize the power of the human intellect to bring rational order to the created world. And in the case of moral theology, to the passions, especially sexual desire. Empathy, on the other hand, is the human capacity to experience with another person her experiences of the world. Empathy feels with the other as unique self. Through empathy one person knows another more fully than by simply relying on observation of that person's behaviors.

As yet, empathy has not been integrated into moral theology. As a result, theological assertions up till now have favored the rational control of the human passions, rather than compassion for the human struggle to integrate our passions into our behaviors. This is especially the case with our compulsive sexual instincts, which are clearly an evolutionary development for the purpose of continuing life-forms on Earth. Thus, sexual intercourse is said to be moral only if exercised between one male and one female committed to each other for life, whose sexual difference is capable of producing a child whom they will parent. Empathy, on the other hand, recognizes the limitations in our human struggle with sexual passions and the gift of humility in our personal relationships.

Sexual Desire

Science shows that the desire to have multiple sexual partners is part of our evolutionary development. In the face of that evolutionary trait, the legal definition of marriage as a covenant between one man and one woman was an attempt to bring order to human sexual desire. That legal definition has roots in the empathic desire by Christians to order their lives and society according to their relationship with Christ. In the Christian scriptures, the analogy of the Church as a community of faith having only one bridegroom, who is Christ, reset the pattern for Christian marriage as monogamy. The relationship between Christ and his bride, the Church, became the model for Christian monogamous, faithful, and loving marriage between a man and a woman.[66]

Before the development of monogamy, polygamy appeared in most cultures, including Judaism, to be the best rational option for the care of persons in their sexual relationships and for the children who were the result of those relationships. Jewish law on monogamy developed after Christianity became the dominant religion in Mediterranean societies and Europe. Twentieth century civil decisions to allow marriage between persons of the same sex were motivated by an empathic desire to find a rational ordering of sexual passion for the sake of the good of the such persons and their society.

Science and theology can agree that the integration of our human passions is essential for the healthy development of interpersonal relationships and of human society. However, the rational ordering

---

66. Ephesians 5:21-32.

of one's sexual desire can easily become a condemnation of the essentially compulsive nature of human sexuality. From my experience as a certified sexual addiction therapist, passions must not be condemned simply because of their power to move us toward action. Sexual compulsion is not the result of sin but of evolution, as is our ability to integrate our passionate responses through empathy, experiencing the effects on another person of our own behaviors.

Human sexual desire, if it is to lead to the wellbeing of self and others, demands that we struggle to attain balance in our relationships. This requires integrating our passions, by both our empathic and logical thinking processes, for the sake of the good of the whole to which we belong. Balancing our passions with empathy allows the tangible image of God to grow into the likeness of the creator who loves us. Struggling to achieve such balance between body and spirit is the path that brings us to likeness with the creator, the path to loving one another as God loves us.

The description of marriage in Genesis expresses this balance between desire and fidelity. The man and woman are flesh and bone, one of the other. "That is why a man leaves his father and mother and clings to his wife, and the two of them become one body. The man and his wife were both naked, yet they felt no shame."[67] Despite this balanced metaphor, some have read the title "wife" as simply a role the woman is to play in the life of the man. While the story is clearly told from the viewpoint of the male, who leaves father and mother to become one with his wife, the difference between them is presented as the basis for the unitive power of their sexuality. Eve is not created simply so that she can play a role in Adam's life. The creator gives the reason for her creation, "It is not good that the man be alone. I will make a suitable partner for him."[68]

---

67. Genesis 2:24-25.
68. Genesis 2:18.

The vision in Genesis is of humanity created not to exist as an isolate but in relationships. Only as two in partnership of being can a man and a woman become one flesh. Both find themselves more truly in their relationship with each other as one embodied humanity differentiated as male and female.[69] Adam will name this other-self *Havah*, Hebrew for "giver of life." Eve will be the mother of all living humans. Here is a second meaning of "they become one body," the begetting of offspring. Sexual difference can generate other embodied beings like the parents.

Although the brain's pleasure center powerfully responds to sexual experiences, the myth does not select sexual arousal as the primary purpose of sex. The Jewish editors of this second myth of creation identify the purpose of sex as relationship building, as attraction and attachment. Sex is for unity between persons, the establishment of a unique relationship of faithfulness in which each may grow as a true self. This is the way empathy orders sexual compulsivity, loving the other as oneself.

The peoples who lived around the Jews engaged in sacred prostitution to increase the land's fertility and their own prosperity. Among the Jews, this was considered a grave offense; sexual arousal was not for a transaction with a prostitute or with God. Rather, sexual arousal was a gift from the creator to foster faithful relationships, not an instrument for manipulation of God or of each other. There are many who have found that, like heterosexual relationships, same-sex relationships are capable of fostering a similar faithfulness as partners in being because of the same human capacity for empathy.

---

69. It is notable that the statement by the creator that it is not good for the "man" to be alone is made about Adam prior to the separation into the two sexes, when Adam is present as the universal particular of humanity. No human being exists as an isolate but only in relationship with other persons and indeed with all creation. Consequently, it may be inferred that designating the female as "wife" includes a realization that it is not good for the female to be alone, any more than it is good for the male. Interrelatedness is the basis for all life, and especially for human life.

The second myth of creation contains a uniquely organic understanding of human relationships, especially sexual ones. There is a sense in other Jewish scriptures that if sex is not used to develop faithful relationships, it will have a negative effect on the rest of nature. For the Jew, unfaithfulness in sexual relationships, especially marriage, was a serious offense and negatively affected the whole of their social coherence and even the land itself. Our sexual behaviors affect the whole to which we belong. Our sexual behaviors have consequences for good and for ill in our relationships with our sexual partners, people in our families and society, and with the whole of which we are a part, our children, economy, social responsibilities, and more.

The importance of the reproductive power made possible by heterosexual difference was recognized in the sacred text as a path to relationship with God, the creator, and to the future that creator wills for humanity. The Jewish people were aware that as descendants of Abraham and Sarah they are born into a relationship with the One God in whom their ancestors placed their faith.[70] As theologian Christine Hayes says, for the Jew the divine will is expressed "in history rather than in nature."[71] This means the divine purpose of our human sexuality will best be known through contextual, situational thinking rather than confined solely to the stoic conceptual thinking associated with natural law arguments. Pope John Paul II attempted to do something similar in developing what is popularly called "the Theology of the Body."[72]

---

70. Genesis 15:1-6.

71. Christine Hayes, What's Divine About Divine Law? (Princeton: University Press, 2015), 2.

72. Through 129 Wednesday afternoon presentations, delivered between 1979 and 1984, Saint John Paul II constructed what is popularly known as the "Theology of the Body" which spawned books, educational programs, and electronic media presentations on the way our human bodies can teach us about our sexuality and our sexuality teach us how to love each other.

God's creative work can only be found within the contingency of the universe and of human life. Marriage is filled day to day with contingencies through which spouses learn to love one another in very contextual ways. While human sexuality from the point of view of science is necessarily compulsive, sexual desire can develop into mutual benevolent love. In Jewish scriptures the relationship between God and the Jewish people is often described by analogy as a relationship between husband and wife. God, the Bridegroom, is faithful to Israel. Israel is constantly called by God to be faithful in return. From the point of view of scripture, the analogy expresses the promise that creation will find its fulfillment not in itself, in isolation, but in a relationship of mutual benevolent love with the One who is God.

Conclusion

The two creation myths which form the first two chapters of Genesis emphasize the relationship between humankind and other life-forms on Earth as the creative work of God. The first myth portrays the fostering of that relationship as the way humankind is to lead all of Earth to sabbath rest with the creator. The second myth carefully portrays the creator's design for human relationships to flourish and for Earth and all its creatures to be a singular home environment for life. Human sexuality is integral to this divine plan, as is the ordered use of sexual desire to form relationships which will benefit the whole to which human life belongs.

In both myths, this whole includes creation's relationship to the creator as the One who fulfills creation. It is God who draws humankind to sabbath rest with the whole of creation and to each one's truest self in our relationships with one another and with God. In these myths, God reveals through creation itself, especially the creation of humans, how life on Earth is to be sustained and led it to its fulfillment. In the next chapter, we reflect on this great work to which we are called and to which both science and religion make their contributions.

Chapter V

Our Work On Earth

The Trait for Religious Thinking

A picture is worth a thousand words. On their way to the moon in December 1972, the crew of the Apollo 17 took a picture whose beauty still astounds. They looked back on Earth shining like a fragile blue marble floating in space. The picture inspires awe. Moved by Earth's beauty, it is easy to grasp the goodness of our common home. Yet its goodness is not without vulnerability, because the temporal nature of any material good evokes fear. Fear is that dimension of awe which causes us discomfort. We fear because we perceive a truth; Earth's beauty and the good that beauty holds can be lost. The empathic allure of Earth's beauty and the goodness of the life it fosters can motivate us to care for Earth and for all the creatures who share our fragile home, because we understand the truth that it can be lost.

Environmental sciences offer significant information about the necessity for this great work, the care of Earth and its creatures. But scientific data alone does not motivate people to act. Motivation and choice arise from a different source in human experience, our empathic experience of beauty which fosters our search into the transcendent. To transcend comes from a Latin verb, *scandere* which means to climb. The prefix, *trans*, means beyond. Of course, there are different ways of describing what it means to climb beyond, to transcend. In evolutionary terms transcendence means something emerges which had not existed previously. Over three billion years ago simple inanimate chemical compounds on Earth apparently became something more, self-sustaining life-forms. That transformation in matter was a radical change, a kind of transcendence whose beauty is manifest now in millions of life-forms.

These life-forms add to the beauty and goodness of Earth, even while they hold a truth about our material world, that living things also die. The allurement of the mystery of life and death constituted a significant dynamic in our human evolution. As early *Homo sapiens* experienced the transcendent qualities of the Cosmos and its life and death mysteries, they enshrined those profound moments in stories that helped make sense of the world around them. These myths express insights that have been handed on by ancient wisdom traditions and are even now shared by current generations.

There is something other, something bigger than we are, that can be perceived through the transcendent qualities in the Cosmos, through its beauty, goodness, and truth. There exists a greater beauty and goodness, a greater truth, a transcendence that remains unseen but which we can experience even in the face of death. Our ability to be allured by the transcendence in the universe was made possible by a trait peculiar to us *Homos sapiens*, a unique trait not found among any of the previous hominin species.

In 2020, Margaret Rappaport and Christopher Corbally, S.J., published their research on the emergence of religious thinking in human evolution. In the preface, the authors state, "Religion is a non-obligatory neurocognitive trait of our species, *Homo sapiens*."[73] Presumably, all *Homo sapiens* now possess the necessary brain structures for religious thinking, though as we well know not everyone utilizes the trait. Like the cognitive capacity for reading, which a person chooses to use or not, a person does not have to engage in religious thinking or the behaviors it motivates. It is a matter of choosing to do so.

The trait for religious thinking and the behaviors it motivates support social cohesion. And it can be mimicked simply because of

---

73. Margaret Boone Rappaport, and Christopher J. Corbally, S.J., The Emergence of Religion in Human Evolution (NY: Routledge, 2020), xi.

a desire to conform to the social expectations that religious thinking supports. Of course religious thinking is not limited to a commitment to personal faith in a deity. But those who participate in a particular religion can simply mimic religious practices to avoid social exclusion. Likewise, people may make a pragmatic decision to mimic religious practices that benefit social welfare, like care of the poor, even though they do not participate in religious credal beliefs or such practices as prayer and community worship.

The human trait for religious thinking, as the authors present it, is the basis for the evolution of world religions, because it seeks ways of being in relationship with what is beautiful, good, and true. These transcendent qualities in creation point to the greater whole to which the individual parts belong. That is why Rappaport and Corbally comment that if religious thinking is employed for any other purpose than being in relationship with the whole, such as political or economic advantage or the denigration of others, it is no longer religion in the sense the authors mean.[74]

The authors believe religious thinking is connected to a more ancient trait among hominins, that for moral thinking. They believe moral thinking developed among a previous species of hominins, *Homo habilis*, as they began to control and use fire. Around a fire, our ancestors could have made group choices to benefit the members of the group. The authors say that this kind of thinking first begun around the hearth "furthers the gifts of life and well-being, supports the social group, and helps to give all participants hope for the future."[75] Religious thinking, however, is a different trait developed over subsequent eons among *Homo sapiens*. Religious thinking can inform moral thinking with an expanded vision of the whole to which we belong and motivate the choice to participate in the care of that greater whole.

---

74. Ibid.
75. Rappaport and Corbally, 108.

Specifically, the trait of religious thinking manifests as "a persistent goal to experience the numinous, the supernatural, that which appears to humans as outside their everyday life, above it, around it, at its foundation."[76] This trait developed through structural changes in the brain of *Homo sapiens*. Those changes included the repurposing both of existing brain structures already evolved in previous *hominin* species and neurocognitive traits inherited from our earlier *hominin* ancestors.

For instance, a portion of the parietals, the *precuneus*, is used for spatial/temporal reckoning. It was presumably employed by *Homo erectus* in scavenging meat, the consumption of which allowed the growth of *hominin* brains, and later by *Homo habilis* to develop hunting skills, the fruit of which furthered growth in *hominin* brain size. The same *precuneus* is used for a new purpose by *Homo sapiens*. We use the *precuneus* to travel supernatural space, to pursue the transcendent through religious thinking.[77] To accommodate structural changes in the enlarged *hominin* brain, the skull evolved among *Homo sapiens* to its current globular shape. This, in part, is why the authors believe previous species of *hominins* did not have the trait for religious thinking because their skulls lacked the globular form.

Religious thinking became foundational to the ongoing evolution of *Homo sapiens* as persons who seek spiritual transcendence. It was manifest in the development of the religions and the cultures they sustained. Consequently, one might wonder if the numinous, already inherent in the Cosmos from the beginning, is evidence of an intention of the creator for the evolution of religious thinking. Was it not the creator's intent to bring about irreversible evolutionary transformation through the human trait for religious thinking, precisely so that we could both become aware of the transcendent and through the transcendent in creation, become aware of God?

---

76. Rappaport and Corbally, xi.
77. Rappaport and Corbally, chapter 6.

However one may answer that question, it is apparent that by informing our moral choices, religious thinking can now motivate our work for the sustainability of the planet we inhabit and its life-forms.

In 1985, Jake Garn orbited Earth aboard the space shuttle and had a numinous experience which he recalled thirty years later as a retired U.S. Senator. He said, "It's impossible to explain to people what it's like to look back and see the entire planet. It was a life changing experience."[78] That experience has since been given a name, "The Overview Effect." The perspective of the astronaut, viewing Earth floating in space, occasioned an awareness of the numinous character of our planet. At the same time as Garn's flight, we were wrestling with the observable consequences of the human degradation of Earth's environment and the extinction of multitudes of species. His experience of the overview effect allowed Garn and other astronauts to believe it possible to unite otherwise conflicting human perspectives on the use of Earth and its resources into a planetary society that would protect this "pale blue dot." Our old Earth-bound perception of competing parts in nature was transformed through the overview effect into a perception of the wholeness of life that is Earth and the motivation to preserve it.

The overview effect, developed through space travel and environmental studies, is an example of how empirically based science now offers a new mythic moment of heroic possibility. Our shared experience of the overview effect, an instance of the human brain seeking the numinous, constitutes religious thinking. As a result, we see how religious thinking can affect moral decisions for the common good of Earth and its creatures. Recognizing we are part of nature and that we affect Earth's welfare by our behaviors, we can

---

78. Kelsey Dallas, "Cosmic humility: The spiritual side effects of viewing Earth from outer space," Deseret News, July 27, 2015. https://www.statesboroherald .com/churches/faith/cosmic-humility-the-spiritual-side-effects-of-viewing-earth-from-outer-space/, accessed January 21, 2022.

work for the good of the greater whole to which we belong. This is a new moment of mythic possibility. It is now possible to develop a para-modern culture of environmentalism using science which is open once again to religious thinking.

A para-modern culture combines elements of a previous culture with elements that culture did not include. Our modern western culture is based in large part on science. The scientific method intentionally separated out the influence of motivation and choice in order to engage in testing and verification. The scientific method, which dominated public discussion for several centuries, was not inclined to preserve other life-forms but to exploit them. It has been only somewhat successful recently in motivating environmental consciousness. As a result we understand that sustaining the environment will take more than scientific facts. In the current post-modern, post-secular culture, religious thinking is being invited to provide motivation and foster action for care of the environment.

Religious thinking, which recognizes the numinous in our experience of the world, is once again being invited to participate with science in motivating the care of Earth and its creatures. In the meantime, formal religious thinking, theology, has striven to incorporate the data of empirical science into its understanding of God. Thus, current efforts to create a dialogue between religious traditions and the sciences is bringing about a para-modern culture which integrates science and theology in a new way. This would be a culture "emerging with the distinctive mythology that people acting together can create justice and peace in the world," including the care of Earth and its life-forms.[79]

Religious Environmentalism

The Yale Forum on Religion and Ecology is an international multireligious project contributing to a new academic field and moral

---

79. Arbuckle, 216.

force called "religious environmentalism." The forum seeks the widest inclusion of religious traditions and scientific data. In 2019, Mary Evelyn Tucker and John Grim, who direct the Forum, published a biography of their mentor Thomas Berry.[80] Berry was a Catholic priest and member of the Passionist religious community, who twenty years earlier had addressed in *The Great Work* the potential for religious traditions to cooperate with scientific researchers in supporting environmentalism. Berry wrote,

> The distorted dream of an industrial technological paradise is being replaced by the more viable dream of a mutually enhancing human presence within an ever-renewing organic-based Earth community.[81]

He named this hoped-for moment of realization the Ecozoic Era. He also warned that being a graced moment, it is a gift which demands action lest the moment be lost. Berry was convinced that the welfare of Earth and the creatures who live here is affected by the interaction of its species, especially the actions of humankind. He believed taking joy in Earth and her creatures is the necessary antidote to the devastation of the environment brought on by our pragmatic interests, which were driven over the last several centuries principally by western cultural perspectives. Berry wrote, "The human venture depends absolutely on this quality of awe and reverence and joy in the Earth and all that lives and grows upon the Earth."[82]

A decade and a half later, Berry's ideas were reflected in Pope Francis' encyclical *Laudato Si'* issued in May 2015. The Italian title was taken from the first words of the "Canticle of the Sun," a poem by Francis of Assisi (1181-1226). The poem, known in English as "The Canticle of Brother Sun and Sister Moon," expresses the great

---

80. Mary Evelyn Tucker, John Grim, and Andrew Angyal, Thomas Berry, A Biography (NY: Columbia Press, 2019).
81. Thomas Berry, The Great Work (NY: Belle Tower, 1999), 201.
82. Ibid., 166.

joy Francis took in praising God for all the creatures. Pope Francis wanted to emphasize the same joy humankind can take in the care of Earth and all its creatures. He did so by placing scientific and religious insights about Earth's ecology side by side and noting how they inform and reinforce each other in our human responsibility to care for Earth. The English sub-title of the encyclical is *On Care for Our Common Home.*

His effort was not new. The Pope recalled that his four immediate predecessors had included Earth sciences with religious motivation as essential in the care of Sister Earth. He himself included in *Laudato Si'* the writing of the leader of another Christian Church, Bartholomew, who is the Ecumenical Patriarch of Orthodox Christians. For decades, Bartholomew has championed the moral dimension of Earth ecology, which led to his being called the Green Patriarch. Bartholomew declared that a sin against Earth, the devastation of the environment or the mass extinction of its creatures, is a sin against each other in the human community and against the creator. The Patriarch wrote, "It is our humble conviction that the divine and the human meet in the slightest detail in the seamless garment of God's creation, in the last speck of dust of our planet."[83]

Pope Francis built on that conviction. Originally a bishop in South America, he wanted to highlight the care of Earth's lungs, the Amazon Basin, by holding the Amazon Synod in Rome during October of 2019. The Amazon Basin takes in portions of nine countries: Bolivia, Brazil, Colombia, Ecuador, French Guiana, Guyana, Peru, Suriname, and Venezuela. Bringing together peoples from such a vast region, the Synod focused its attention on the preservation of the Amazon Basin's ecology. The Pope meant to unite all the peoples of the area in this effort, particularly Catholic

---

83. Patriarch Bartholomew, "Global Responsibility and Ecological Sustainability," Closing Remarks, Halki Summit I, Istanbul (20 June 2012), quoted in Laudato Si, note 18.

believers as a practical expression of their faith. Their devotion to God, the creator, was to be expressed by redeeming the basin from ongoing destruction. To do so, the Synod *de facto* implemented the four wisdoms Thomas Berry proposed in <u>The Great Work</u> to guide humankind to a new relationship with the natural world. These are the wisdoms 1) of contemporary science, 2) of indigenous cultures, 3) of women, and 4) of ancient and classical religions or wisdom traditions.

Pope Francis stated he desired to learn how to care for the environment of the Amazon region from its native peoples. In addition to the wisdom of contemporary earth sciences which had been featured in *Laudato Si*, indigenous wisdom was central to the Amazonian synodal process. The Pope wanted to hear from the diverse tribes who have inhabited that vast basin over several millennia. Thus, he included peoples pushed to the peripheries by the incursion of western civilization. Francis reinforced ancient tribal wisdom by recognizing another of Berry's four wisdom sources, the wisdom of women which holds a place of leadership among the Amazonian tribes. Women among these indigenous tribes already have leadership roles both in ecology and in the life of Catholic communities in the Amazon Basin.

The integral presence of these two wisdom sources, both indigenous cultures and women, had proved unsettling to many interests in the region, even to the point of ongoing persecution and murder of indigenous persons and especially of women who continue to champion environmental preservation. The presence of indigenous peoples and especially of women proved unsettling as well to cultural and theological conservatives within the Catholic Church who criticized the Synod. The leadership of women and indigenous peoples was symbolized by indigenous female-fertility statues given place of honor in a local Roman church during the Synod. Some traditionalists declared them pagan idols. Duly scandalized, a few of them summarily tossed the statues into the Tiber, a centuries old means of protest among Romans.

Sadly, the wisdom both of indigenous peoples and of women has been historically denigrated by western cultural hegemony. The conflict during the Amazon Synod over the female statues is an example of such denigration. Christians, strongly affected by western cultural dominance, also express the hegemony of their own religion over indigenous wisdom. Economic interests, especially when supported by religious suppression of local wisdom, treat the Amazon Basin as a region to be conquered for its resources, cattle ranching, and mining. The Basin instead needs to be preserved and cared for as a valued and essential planetary ecosystem.

His Catholic sensibilities led Berry to reject such exclusivism in western political, economic, social, and religious perspectives. Instead, Berry believed wisdom traditions or ancient religions from around the world have much in common in fostering the historical evolution of humanity and human cultures. As such, he believed they could work together to demonstrate the capacity of humans "to achieve the fullness of their own mode of being."[84] Ancient wisdom holds out hope that humankind may live on Earth in union with the other creatures and with each other. This mode of being is possible because ancient wisdom traditions believe our true mode of being exists in relationship with the creator of all.

Differing Metaphysics

There is a theory that religion, like politics, is the cause of conflicts among people. What is conflictual among religions is their metaphysics. A metaphysic is a theory about how everything holds together. Each religion has its own, as does modern science. Because the universe is an interdependent whole, every religious tradition has much in common in the story each tells about the numinous, which

---

84. Berry, 185.

is itself the source of our common experience of transcendence. However, the story each tells about the numinous embodies each tradition's unique experience of the world. A religion's metaphysic, the way it describes the whole to which we belong, often will conflict in some way with that of another religion.

Conflicts not only occur among religious metaphysics but also between them and the story modern science tells. The framework for the modern physical sciences excludes anything that cannot be tested and verified experimentally, and of course many say this necessitates the exclusion of God. Christian theology, on the other hand, views the world from the perspective of a creator who is bringing the universe to completion, which is both present but not yet fulfilled. That means God is the one who brought creation into existence and will bring creation to its fulfillment, which is likeness to God.

Modern science views the world solely through the perspective of physical causes and effects. Therefore, any dialogue between science and religion must be presumed to have some areas of conflict. Conflicts within the Catholic Church are apparent in the negative reaction to the environmental leadership of Pope Francis. Conflicts arose in governmental attempts to deal with a global Covid pandemic, some over the science itself and others over religious objection to how science developed vaccines. Conflict is evident in the writing of scientists like Richard Dawkins whose titles include The God Delusion and Outgrowing God. These conflicts arise because of what we expect to see as we observe things in the Cosmos according to our accepted theory about how everything holds together in the universe.

The perspective of the physical sciences holds that the material world can be comprehensively explained by physical causes alone, which must exclude anything that cannot be tested and verified experimentally. But is that reality? "Perspectival observation," suggests otherwise. "Perspectival observation," a term adopted by Schwartz and Ogilvy in 1979, is used to explain what goes unrecognized in our observation. Scientific observation is not objective in any absolute sense. There are no unconditioned observational facts.[85] That is because by observing something we change the very thing observed. We see what we expect to see in the thing we observe. If the metaphysic of physical sciences holds that the material world can be comprehensively explained by physical causes alone, then a scientist will ultimately seek a theory of everything solely by reconciling those efficient causes. It remains to be seen if that is possible.

Edith Stein, a philosopher of phenomenology, pointed out that by looking only at physical causes and effects scientists were ignoring other phenomena. *Phenomenon* is Greek for "what appears." Stein was a Jewish victim of Auschwitz, a Catholic religious sister and saint known by her religious name as Teresa Benedicta of the Cross. She published her doctoral dissertation in August 1916 "On the Problem of Empathy." In following chapters we will see how empathy is integral for our understanding of the human person. For now, we are interested in how Stein explained the limitation of the metaphysic of the physical sciences and its rational ordering of nature.

Marianne Sawicki wrote extensively on Stein's works. She explains that in a person's stream of consciousness various things appear at the same time and choices are continuously made about what to let go and what to attend.[86] Sawicki sums up Stein's analysis of scientific observation and testing by saying it amounts to subtractive literacy. Material sciences, in order to identify physical causes and effects, first subtract all motivations from the various phenomena they observe. What remains is what they call "scientific data."

---

85. Ronald N. Giere, "The Perspectival Nature of Scientific Observation," June 3, 2015. https://www.researchgate.net/publication/242574702_The_Perspectival _Nature_of_Scientific_Observation, accessed October 24, 2020.
86. Marianne Sawicki, Philosophy of Psychology and the Humanities (The Collected Works of Edith Stein, vol. 7), ICS Publications, February 2016.

That means all personal motivation and choice has been purged, all presumed personal bias eliminated from the data the sciences use to understand the order of the Cosmos and its phenomena. That includes any need for a creator choosing to create or a creature choosing to respond. Paradoxically, this also means the scientific data, which describes physical causes without attending to motivations, is itself motivated to do so. The result is called objective data, but that is never absolutely so.

To arrive at what is called objective data, the metaphysic of modern science motivates scientists to select the laws of nature alone to explain the contents of the universe and their interrelationships. The physical sciences seek to eliminate the bias of motivation and choice in order to seek only physical causes. As we saw in the first chapter, Stephen Hawking believed the fixed laws of nature are sufficient to explain the Big Bang and there is consequently no need for a creator at the Cosmos' beginnings. However, there is a different approach to scientific cosmology being developed in what Elias Kruger calls the new post-secular culture. He says cosmology is

> currently undergoing a shift from natural to human sciences. The implications of scientific research into natural evolution developed into research on the evolution of the Cosmos and led to the theory of the Big Bang. Driven by the Anthropic Principle, the focus now has shifted to studies in neuroscience, to questions of personhood and the cognitive science of religion. The field has zoomed in from the macro view of cosmology to the micro view of anthropology.[87]

In other words, the study of cosmology has broadened from emphasis on the sciences of physics and mathematics to include

87. Elias Kruger, "Integrating Technology and Religion in a Post-Secular World," a post on AI Theology, https://www.aitheology.com/2021/02/17/integrating-technology-and-religion-in-a-post-secular-world/ accessed October 25, 2020.

scientific study of anthropology, the study of the human person from multiple perspectives, including theological anthropology.

Conclusion

What science currently understands about the New Story of the evolving Cosmos is in different stages of dealing with the post-modern and post-secular integration of science and religion. Both have something to contribute to how we understand environmentalism. For example, Brian Swimme is a scientist who began as a mathematician, did his doctoral research on singularities, and now teaches cosmology at the California Institute of Integral Studies. Swimme says the physical sciences now provide the empirical ground for dialogue between science, wisdom traditions, and human anthropology to explore what he calls the powers coursing through the Universe and each of us.

Swimme's resultant cosmology is a philosophy of nature rooted in scientific observation of the Cosmos. He believes that there are powers in the universe that can be observed in each of its parts, and these powers are what the ancient religious or wisdom traditions observed as well. Swimme invites the use of the observations of the modern physical sciences as the empirical basis for theological explanations of our human search for the numinous. We will examine his theory in the next chapter.

Chapter VI

Seeking the Numinous

The Powers of the Cosmos

Cosmology at one time was a physical science, the study of the physical forces within the universe. It has evolved into a philosophy of nature, now called the new cosmology. As a philosophy of nature, the new cosmology considers not just the data of the physical sciences but their relationship with the data of other disciplines. The hoped-for result is to provide fuller meaning and understanding of the interrelatedness of everything that makes up the Cosmos. However, like every philosophy, its underlying assumptions need to be examined.

Consider allurement, one of ten interconnected powers Brian Swimme observes in the Cosmos. Earthlings are allured by the vastness of the Cosmos, the peculiar makeup of cosmic space/time, and by the multitude of stars which shine beyond our sun. The allure of these stars motivated the discovery that many visible stars are in fact whole galaxies containing an average of a hundred billion stars each, some of which are newly born, others ever so slowly flickering out, and still others powerfully exploding, even able to threaten our very existence from lightyears away.[88] And among the stars there are countless planets, some recognized as earthlike and perhaps able to support life as we know it, most not at all. Awed that over ninety-five percent of the Cosmos is dark matter and dark energy, we can only

---

88. Supernova explosions have been implicated in triggering mass extinctions on Earth, like the one that occurred 2.6 million years ago or the Permian-Triassic extinction 252 million years ago that was the most devastating to Earth's biota, killing about 96 percent of all marine species and 70 percent of all terrestrial vertebrate species. Cf. www.airspacemag.com/daily-planet/threat-stellar-explosions-180974252/ accessed October 25, 2020.

observe the interactions of the visible five percent. Yet even that darkness allures as it exerts gravity within the Cosmos.

Swimme says gravity, the weakest of the physical forces, is an expression of Cosmic allurement. At the subatomic level, charged particles exert gravitational attraction. At the macro level galaxies are drawn to each other, so that what may have been two trillion galaxies in the distant past already have coalesced over the eons toward half that number at present. According to the most recent measurements by the Hubble Space Telescope, in about two billion years our galaxy, the Milky Way, will merge with the nearest galaxy, Andromeda, which eventually will set off collisions of multiple stars.[89] At a more local level, the planets in our solar system are allured by the sun, the moon by Earth, the seas in their tidal rhythms by the moon. However, is allurement, which is present as a physical power of the Cosmos, also present as a transcendent power able to move things toward fulfillment in their relationships with each other? It appears so to Swimme.

Swimme sees physical needs and pleasures as manifestations of allurement. Bees and hummingbirds are allured by nectar, life-forms through sexual urges, children by apples in a neighbor's orchard, and humans by various passions. Allurement in each of these instances draws one thing to another. Swimme thus appears to broaden the scientific method beyond a search for physical causation. If we include physical needs, pleasures, and passions in the cosmic power of allurement, we are also including motivation and choice. Just so, Swimme has included motivation and choice among the Cosmic powers. In doing so, has he made room for something besides efficient causality, that is cause and effect, in his perspective as a scientist? Our choices concerning the fulfillment of our needs,

89. https://www.cbsnews.com/news/andromeda-galaxy-will-collide-with-milky-way/ accessed October 24, 2020.

pleasures, and passions, while initially motivated by physical impulses, also depend on our personal motivations and intentions. Together these may lead to personal transcendence, as compassion or love.

Accordingly, Swimme believes, the pursuit of each person's unique passion (the personal power of allurement) leads to love. But we must be aware that love is not an effect caused directly by passion. Whether passion leads to love depends on the kind of motivation which focuses the power of our passions toward action. Love requires more than a physical or emotional reaction. The fullest capacity for human love is a choice based upon motivation and intentionality. To choose what and how to love, in a way that cares for the other as for oneself, takes both moral thinking and religious thinking. Moral thinking to discern how to accomplish the good of the whole to which one belongs. Religious thinking to expand our perception of that whole and motivate us to achieve its welfare. Ultimately, love is a transcendent expression of self and not simply a physical experience. Swimme thinks, as do various wisdom traditions, that it is through love that all the powers that course through us can be united in the service of the wholeness of the Cosmos.

Swimme clearly understands that the subtractive literacy (eliminating all motivation) of the physical sciences is not enough to motivate people to work for an environmentally sustainable Earth. Therefore, he has reintroduced the motivation of love so that environmentalism may be rooted in a search for the transcendent. Swimme, like his mentor Thomas Berry, invites the great wisdom traditions to support this new adventure. To do so, religious traditions must accomplish two things. Firstly, root their reflections on the numinous in the empirical evidence available through science and then effectively motivate the care of Earth and its creatures through love. Importantly, among the many contradictory passionate interests of persons and societies, religious traditions can help clarify the very meaning of love.

Let us consider passions. The ability of passion to bring forth love was previously considered to be a discussion conducted by theology or philosophy, and not one conducted by the physical sciences. While passion can lead to loving something, our human story has proved that passion is equally capable of giving life or dealing death in the name of the beloved. To be love in truth, love must be motivated toward the good of the whole with which one lives, and that includes the numinous. As Pope Benedict XVI wrote, "Truth is the light that gives meaning and value to charity ... Without truth, charity degenerates into sentimentality."[90]

If love of Earth and its creatures is to be more than sentimentality, it must be informed by truth. The natural sciences seek truth about natural causes. Neurosciences seek to understand the truth about human motivations. The discipline of religious thinking (theology) seeks truth about the deeper transcendent relationships revealed within nature. Only through a dialogue among these disciplines can love for Earth and its creatures become love in truth.

As an example, Pope Francis understands the power of allurement as the way God draws humankind into unity with Godself, each other, and Earth. This includes the unity of the Church with the rest of humanity. The Pope told young people, the Church does not grow out of proselytizing, but rather out of attraction and one's life witness.[91] In both Catholic and Orthodox theology, the Church exists in the world not for itself but for the completion of creation by accompanying and assisting all things to their divinely promised

90. Pope Benedict XVI, "Caritas in veritate," an encyclical published June 29, 2009, https://www.vatican.va/content/benedict-xvi/en/encyclicals/documents/
91. Pope Francis, "The Church Does Not Grow Out of Proselytizing ... It Grows Out of Attraction," Christian News Network (December 24, 2019).

fulfillment. If persons use the power of allurement for any other reason than unity with the whole to which one belongs, they are neither using the trait for religious thinking nor loving in truth.

In "The Universe is a Green Dragon," Swimme synthesized the ten powers he sees in the Cosmos as a new matrix for ancient wisdom traditions, saying,

> We have a vast new empirically grounded story of the universe, one that explodes beyond any previous telling of reality, one that encompasses all peoples because it is rooted in concrete experience. Within this emerging story, each tradition will flower beyond telling in fruitful interaction with the rest, and together we can continue our journey to our fullest destiny.[92]

As one can see from our reflection on Genesis in previous chapters, Swimme is correct that an empirically grounded story of the universe provides a new and dynamic matrix for the reinterpretation of the myths of ancient wisdom traditions. Grounded in empirical science, the new story of the evolution of the universe is also a new mythic story for our contemporary age. His optimism for the potential progress of human beings toward a planetary community based on this new myth is obvious. Of course, Swimme cannot say what our fullest destiny might be because it is still beyond the event horizon of our existence and must yet unfold.

Cataclysm and Emergence

If we are to form some idea of the future, it is important to look at Swimme's approach to two other cosmic powers, cataclysm and emergence. He defines cataclysm as the power of destruction. We live in a universe where things break down. As such, cataclysm

---

92. Brian Swimme, "The Universe Is A Green Dragon: Reading the meaning in the cosmic story," in The New Story, Winter 1985/86 (Context Institute, 1986). https://www.context.org/iclib/ic12/swimme/, accessed October 20, 2020.

appears to open a rupture in the seamlessness of the universe and in our very existence. When looked at alone, it could very well give that impression. But the powers in the universe work together according to Swimme. Cataclysm when paired with emergence takes on its own significance as part of the goodness of creation. Emergence is the power of creativity, how the universe transcends itself. Swimme shows that these two powers work in tandem. He points out that the carbon and oxygen needed for life on Earth emerged in vast amounts over five billion years ago in stars that exploded, scattering these elements into the Cosmos, and making possible Earth's eventual formation. Thus, the power of cataclysm is essential for the emergence of life on Earth, just as the decomposition of plants is essential for the development of soil in which other plants may grow.

Entropy is a natural condition in the universe. It is the lack of order or predictability within systems. Entropy is the gradual decline into disorder and the ultimate disintegration that haunts material systems and all life-forms. Swimme locates entropy within the power of cataclysm and does so as he describes cataclysm as the prerequisite for emergence. This scientific perspective on cataclysm and emergence provides an essential opening for religious thinking. For instance, it seems to provide an empirical grounding for the religious practice known in Tibetan Buddhism as "sky burial."

In a region where the ground is mostly rock, and wood for a coffin or cremation is scarce, exposure to the elements allows the body of a deceased relative to provide sustenance for life. Since there is no longer life in the flesh of the deceased, religious thinking allows the de-fleshing of the deceased by vultures or other animals as a final act of compassion. Sky burial is an act of compassion offered to other sentient creatures by reducing their struggle to find nourishment. Ancient wisdom traditions, such as Buddhism, know death is part of the cycle of life. The death of weak members of a species makes room for healthier members to thrive and evolve. Some First Nation

American tribes met the loss of a member with the consoling belief that one person leaves to make space for another to come.

Death is nature's way of progressing. So, Swimme concludes that existence is only given to each part of the Cosmos for its specified time and purpose. In this way he allows for theology's take on existence being purposeful and not meaningless. As a result, he opens space for the time and purpose of an individual's life. Nonetheless, death occasions grief, a sense of loss, because it is the loss of a personal self. We experience the reality of death as both personal vulnerability and loss, whether the death is ours or another's, natural or intentional.

As a result, every death reveals the suffering and vulnerability to which all sentient beings are subject both by natural forces and human motivation. Every death raises two questions: 1) what is the purpose of suffering among all the sentient beings across the ages of evolution, and 2) is death the end of a person or is some transcendence possible through death? In the face of these questions, suffering and death appear to human experience to be a form of evil in creation which we cannot escape. It is the diminishment or loss of a good, the loss of personal security and even of existence itself. Death in this material universe calls into question the goodness of creation and the intention of the creator.

If ancient wisdom traditions enter a dialogue with Swimme's presentation of cataclysm and emergence, there are multiple possible outcomes. By our emergence from the cataclysm of death we might enter more fully into the whole to which we belong, which describes Hinduism's belief in a soul's return to the One Great Soul. For a Buddhist, the cataclysm of death can free a person from desire and allow the eventual emergence into enlightened peace, Nirvana. Christianity itself is rooted in the cataclysm of the personal death of Jesus and his emergence as the risen Christ. For Christianity, the ultimate transcendence of every person must follow this same path. Resurrection, living for God alone forever, is the emergence of one's truest self. One emerges through the cataclysm of death fully one with all that is. That means one also emerges as the truest expression of self in conscious and active union with all that is. Or perhaps put more simply, the transcendence sought by Christians in resurrection from the dead does not cancel out self-awareness but perfects it in an ongoing adventure of discovery in union with the majesty of God.

Consistent with the theological meaning of grace, a gift, Swimme believes existence itself "is a pure receiving that brings with it conditions determined by the larger course of earthly events."[93] However, he goes on to say, death, which is one of those conditions, "is the price we pay for life" without which "the whole of life might tend toward the trivial." This appears to be one resolution of suffering, at least for self-reflective beings; suffering teaches us to value beauty, goodness, and truth. That also may be necessary in modern highly developed cultures, as Swimme points out. But if death is the price we pay for life, is existence a transaction, and if so, who receives the payment? What then of those who live in misery? Is their death freedom from pain, oppression, and misery, and if so, can their existence be called a gift, or is life a curse for them? World religions have grappled with these questions for millennia.[94]

The certainty of death surely can serve as a remedy for lifestyles which trivialize human existence. But such conscious realization neither necessarily occurs nor does it resolve the scandal of death itself. Death calls up all our other vulnerabilities, like poverty, sickness, injustice, and violence which blur the line between natural

93. Brian Swimme and Thomas Berry, The Universe Story: From the primordial flaring forth to the Ecozoic era, a celebration of the unfolding of the cosmos (San Francisco: Harper, 1992), 248.
94. Cf. The Book of Job and the podcast commentary, accessed September 30, 2020 at https://podcasts.apple.com/us/podcast/the-place-we-find-ourselves/

cataclysm and moral evils. For the living human, death challenges us with the potential loss of existence as a corporeal being, an embodied center of personal individual consciousness. Death signals a consequent loss of all the relationships through which an embodied person defines herself.

Sadly, it is precisely to preserve ourselves in the face of these vulnerabilities that we abuse Earth and its creatures, especially other humans. Our desire for food security, for instance, has led to the use of single source crops which require artificial fertilizers and more water than indigenous varieties. In turn, we use more carbon-based fuels to create fertilizers and rely on limited local water resources. This has the effect of destroying wetlands and species. To preserve our own security, we turn away refugees fleeing poverty, drought, and war. We even initiate wars of self-interest against less powerful peoples. Thus cataclysm occasions moral evils.

Wisdom traditions have grappled with the issues of vulnerability, suffering, and death by asking powerful theological questions. Why would a creator make a material universe which is subject to entropy and thus bring suffering and death to sentient beings? Is death something that we have caused by our misbehaviors, our sin, or is it imposed by a deity who simply saves eternal existence for Self? If beauty and goodness are reflections in creation of the attributes of a creator, how does death express these transcendent qualities? Is death necessarily the end of our existence; is there personal transcendence of some kind beyond death? Where do we begin to seek the answers to these questions about suffering and death, the possibility of personal transcendence, and a creator's motivations for allowing the suffering of all living creatures?

Conclusion

These questions had a nascent emergence among hominins as early as 300,000 years ago as they purposefully buried their dead, and perhaps among the still disputed burials by even earlier hominin groups. Moral thinking about the welfare of individuals in the group was apparently operative in such burials. However, purposeful burials seem to have begun with the evolution of the trait for religious thinking which gave rise to thinking about transcendence and even life beyond death.

The earliest undisputed purposeful burial of the species *Homo sapiens*, discovered so far, dates back 100,000 years.[95] Those skeletal remains, discovered in Israel, were stained with red ochre. Any purposeful burial, as one with ritual-like use of ochre, points to the human ability to feel loss and in the face of loss to seek the numinous. The experience of death among *Homo sapiens* who possessed the trait for religious thinking occasioned an evolution in human consciousness. Personal existence, as far as we can know it, can be rescinded. We can and will die. How this truth motivates us in our choice of a path to transcendence is the topic of the following chapter.

---

95. https://humanorigins.si.edu/evidence/behavior/burial/qafzeh-oldest-intentional-burial, accessed 9/6/2021.

Chapter VII

The Rupture

From Where Came Death?

Upon entering a patient's room, what is the first thing a nurse looks for? The answer may appear simple but think again. We are so used to rationalizing, imposing order on things through conceptual thinking, that few persons can select the most obvious answer. And what is that? The nurse looks for a body! Looking for a body is an example of situational thinking. The presence of a body signals whether the room is occupied or not, whether the patient is in bed or not, asleep or not, feeling better or not, is safe or not, is alive or not. In this material universe, the body of each living thing is the symbol of a unique existence. As such, your body is the sacrament of your personal presence; it makes you present. Your body is the symbol of the mystery of your personhood; no one else has your body or is you. Your human body is thus sacred; it is set aside to be uniquely you. We even treat the body with respect after a person dies.

At the same time, we live each day with the threat of exile from our body, exile from our self. We perceive being alive as a good, and we experience death as the loss of that good we call existence. In the face of this inevitable loss, we must choose how to live. How we choose to live with the certainty of personal death is the template we use to face every other vulnerability in life. The truth is, knowing we will die, we make choices in life that are responses to this inevitable rupture in our relationship with the whole to which we belong. This is the fundamental context for the Genesis myth of the sin of Adam and Eve. How in the face of the threat of death did the first *Homo sapiens* make their choice to live life; and consequently, how do we, their descendants, continue to do so in the struggles of our lives? These choices affect not only relationships within the human

107

community but also our relationships with other creatures, Earth itself, and God, the creator.

The kind of choices we make in the face of the certainty of death can be divided into two kinds. Either we care for the welfare of the whole to which we belong, or we care for ourselves at the expense of that whole of which we are a part. The first is a choice to love; the second is called sin.

Sin is *hamartia* in Greek or "missing the mark." The meaning is simple. Sin is the failure to live the goodness we are, the form given us by the creator. To be in the image of God is to have a share in the goodness of the creator. To share that goodness in the care of Earth and its creatures is to grow in the likeness of God. This is true because in Genesis God's act of creating is a threefold activity. God shares being by bringing into concrete existence what did not exist, sustains creation as it diversifies, and leads it to its fulfillment in God. In the Genesis story of the original sin, Adam and Eve miss the mark. They choose to care for themselves at the expense of the whole to which they belong. That choice ultimately is expressed in using death as an instrument against other life-forms, thus humanity choosing death over life. That missing the mark is played out as a rupture in all our relationships, with self, God, and each other.

Any Christian understanding of sin and its relationship to death begins with our interpretation of the myth of the original sin, which is found in the third chapter of Genesis. In early Christian history, the myth received two interpretations, both of which remain normative among Catholic, Orthodox, Anglican, Lutheran, and Reformed Church Christians. In Western Christianity, among both Roman Catholics and Protestants, the predominate interpretation was developed by Augustine (354-430 C.E.), Bishop of Hippo in North Africa. It is the one that is most familiar in our culture. We will reinterpret it in the following chapter in light of modern empirical science. In this chapter we will set up the background for that reinterpretation.

108

Among Eastern Christians (Catholic and Orthodox, Byzantine and Oriental) the normative interpretation is older and appears in the writings of Irenaeus (about 140-203 C.E), Bishop of Lyon in what today is France. Irenaeus was Greek speaking, originally from Eastern Turkey. These two interpretations have coexisted for at least sixteen centuries, with one or the other being given precedence by different churches and various theologians. In this chapter we are setting the stage for a reinterpretation of the original sin to be presented in the following chapter. Our reinterpretation has much more in common with Irenaeus. But for now we must examine Augustine's interpretation which influences most of our contemporary understanding of an original sin.

In his *Confessions*, Augustine examined the many choices he made over his lifetime. In his early life, Augustine believed the material world was created as a place of conflict between good and evil, darkness and light.[96] This conflict was evident in the tendencies of the body, especially the desires for self-preservation and for sexual intercourse. These desires seemed to conflict with the desire of his mind to serve higher goals, specifically the life of the intellect. When he later became a Christian, Augustine interpreted the myth of original sin through the lens of his own disordered feelings and relationships. He interpreted the original sin of Adam and Eve as the cause of moral disorder in the subsequent choices made by their descendants. Augustine understood that this conflict or disorder within himself provided the motivation for choices that were sinful. But he went further.

Modern science tells us that the cataclysm we see in nature, its disorder, is caused by entropy. Entropy is defined as the gradual and inevitable decline into disorder of any material existence. All life-

---

96. Augustine was a proponent of Manicheanism before being baptized into the Catholic Church by Ambrose of Milan. Manicheanism was derived from Zoroastrianism, a dualistic Iranian religion of light and darkness. Manicheans held that matter was evil and spirit good. Escape from the material world was the escape from evil.

forms on Earth experience death because all material within the Cosmos is subject to entropy. The body of a vibrant self-reflective human being is destined through aging, illness, and death to decompose into the elements which make it up. Death in turn becomes the symbol for our decline through the multiple vulnerabilities to which our bodies are subject. But at the time of Augustine such scientific knowledge was unavailable. Consequently, Augustine believed entropy, this disorder in the universe and so in his own body, was caused by the original sin of Adam and Eve. Death came into the world as the result of sin.

Augustine interpreted Genesis to teach that God, in creating Earth and the heavens, established order out of chaos or formlessness by giving order to chaos or form to what was formless. The sin of Adam and Eve introduced disorder into God's orderly creation. The consequence of their sin also brought moral disorder to the bodily desires of their descendants, even as it caused natural disorder in all creation.

According to Augustine's interpretation, death had not existed in creation until the sin of Adam and Eve. God punished their sin with bodily death, the dissolution into disorder of our material bodies. Their descendants inherited the same punishment. Furthermore, he believed the disorder found in nature, especially death, is caused by the moral disorder Adam and Eve brought into creation by their sin. By declaring sin to be the cause of both moral and natural disorder in the world, Augustine believed he was following the teaching presented three hundred years earlier by the Apostle Paul.

In his letter to the Romans, Paul wrote, "Therefore, just as through one person [Adam, the universal particular] sin entered the world, and through sin, death, and thus death came to all, inasmuch as all sinned."[97] Thus, the Augustinian tradition is that death entered the world as a punishment for sin. But Paul was teaching that moral

---

97. Romans 5:12.

110

disorder entered the world through Adam's sin. Adam's descendants, understood to be a corporate whole with him, were affected by his sin and have kept on sinning. Moral disorder has remained in the world since the time of our first parents.

For Paul, the fact that everyone dies is evidence that everyone is a corporate whole with Adam who sinned. But Paul does not say the moral disorder of sin caused natural disorder and death to enter creation. Instead, Paul is interpreting how God describes the relationship between Adam and Earth that has been established by Adam's sin. After Adam's sin, God says,

> Cursed be the ground because of you! In toil shall you eat its yield all the days of your life. Thorns and thistles shall it bring forth to you, as you eat of the plants of the field. By the sweat of your face shall you get bread to eat, until you return to the ground, from which you were taken; for you are dirt, and to dirt you shall return[98]

All humans, beginning with our first parents, come from Earth and return to the dust of the Earth. This is the created natural order that includes death. However, any disorder, natural or moral, is interpreted as a punishment from God by humans who serve their own self-interests rather than the whole of which we are a part. Death, and all the natural disorder in creation, is interpreted by those who sin as a curse, because it upends their self-interests.

Paul's intent in Romans is to proclaim the remedy God had in mind before the creation of the world, the remedy for both the natural disorder that arises in the contingency in the universe and the moral disorder that arises through sin. Paul says,

> For creation was made subject to futility, not of its own accord but because of the one who subjected it, in hope that creation

---

98. Genesis 3:17-19.

itself would be set free from slavery to corruption and share in the glorious freedom of the children of God.[99]

Creation was created good, though incomplete. In the plan of God, creation is unable to fulfill itself, so that by the death and resurrection of Christ creation might find its fulfillment in God. Paul uses the idea of corporate humanity to set up the contrast between the sin of Adam and the salvation that comes from Christ, the second Adam. In the first Adam, one person sinned and all followed suit becoming sinners. In Adam, we also inherited the natural order of death, which is the result of entropy.

However, Paul's notion that God subjected creation to futility allows us, in view of contemporary science, to understand that entropy and death are part of creation, and these will find their completion through Christ's resurrection. But what do we make of Paul's teaching that in Christ, the second Adam, one person suffered death so that all can find forgiveness of sin and fullness of life? Christ's bodily death brought together the natural order in the universe and the moral disorder of sin that plagues humankind. The natural order is that all living things die. The moral disorder is that Christ's death was an act of violent victimization brought about by humans seeking their own interests.

Paul teaches elsewhere that all human sin was gathered by God into the violent victimization of Christ on the cross. As the second Adam, Christ is the corporate person in whom all human sin was summed up and nailed to a cross, so that our debt would be canceled.[100] For Paul, the plan of God before the creation of the world was to bring creation which was subject to cataclysm to its completion through a new emergence in the person of Jesus the Christ, through his resurrection from the dead.

---

99. Romans 8:19-23.
100. 2 Corinthians 5:21 and Colossians 2:14.

Augustine, on the one hand, understood Paul to mean that death, the symbol of physical disorder, entered the world because of Adam's sin. But if death entered creation as a punishment for sin, either God brought something new into creation because of sin, or the moral evil of sin itself caused the natural evil of death. Following the later line of thought, many have understood Augustine to teach that moral evil is the cause of natural evil. Not only that, but they also think because of the disorder in material things introduced by sin, we have disorder in our bodily passions that leads to more sin. But that seems to be Augustine's interpretation and not Paul's intent.

Paul does indicate that, since sin entered creation, our passions have been set on defending ourselves from the punishment of death. This is evident in the way Paul uses the term "flesh" and opposes it to "spirit." Sin continues to spread as humans defend themselves from every perceived vulnerability to their existence in the flesh, and we do so at the expense of each other and the whole to which we belong. Paul writes,

> The concern of the flesh is death… [and the result] is hostility toward God; the flesh does not submit to the law of God, nor can it; and those who are in the flesh [seeking only to live for the sake of preserving their body] cannot please God.[101]

Here, Paul is leading to a discussion of God's remedy. He wants his Christian readers to know that they do not have to live according to the flesh because they have received the Spirit, the power of Christ's resurrection. It is the Spirit who will bring about the healing of moral disorder and ultimately of natural disorder. This healing will be the work of the Spirit of God from within human persons and so from within the Cosmos of which humans are a part. For Paul, the first step in healing each person is the gift of faith which works through love. Faith establishes a person as a member of the community, or church, which is interrelatedness in Christ. From

---

101. Romans 8:6.

within that communion, the members can actively accompany other persons and, indeed, every creature to fulfillment in the same Christ.

Augustine's interpretation of Genesis and Romans continues to control much of the understanding of western Christians. Many think that natural evil, the loss of the good available in creation, is caused by moral evil. Natural death, along with the natural disorders of floods and volcanic eruptions, of famine and disease continue to be thought of as punishment for moral evil. This whole line of Augustinian thought is an extension of Augustine's interpretation of original sin which he based on the idea that creation at its beginning was complete, perfectly ordered, and deathless. But science shows it was not.

It is true, however, that Paul does teach that natural and moral disorder are related in God's plan for the fulfillment of creation. Nature will be freed from natural disorder (entropy) when humans are freed from moral disorder, sin. That of course requires that all persons must first experience death, natural disorder, and then be raised to life, a state in which there will be no more sin or death. In that case, natural and moral disorder would both be overcome by resurrection to eternal life which was the creator's intent in creating this material world.

A Different View on Human Life

Irenaeus allowed for this divine intention by taking a more developmental approach to the way God deals with creation, one which is more compatible with the current scientific evidence of evolution. We were created in the divine image but by our Spirit inspired growth and struggle we may attain true likeness to God. As part of an evolving creation, humans are subject to the weakness of the flesh which makes us afraid of death and other vulnerabilities. This fear moves us to seek our own self-interests at the expense of each other and all life on Earth. But as a preoccupation with the world, sin is merely "a stumbling block to our spiritual progress, an obstruction to our development into full spiritual maturity" in likeness to God.[102] Paul made this point in his letter to the Romans.

The concern of the flesh is death, but the concern of the spirit is life and peace... you are not in the flesh; on the contrary, you are in the spirit, if only the Spirit of God dwells in you.[103]

The image of God was created in us when we were given existence as humans. This image of God is the goodness we are, which includes the capacity to intentionally move beyond ourselves, to share our goodness with others. But the *likeness* of God is fashioned in us throughout our lifelong struggle to live by going out of ourselves, *ekstasis*, in the virtuous life the Spirit of God empowers us to live.

For a Christian, virtues are our imitation of the behaviors of love we see in Christ Jesus, behaviors toward God, others, and self within the world as it was created by God which includes entropy and death. These virtues are animated within us by the Spirit of God. Thus, the Spirit's work in us is to sustain and bring to fulfillment what God created, in us and in the world. Sin's remedy is found in God's compassion toward us as sinners, who nonetheless, bear the divine *image*. Sin is inevitable, because we have free will and struggle in our relationships, as we make our choices among various goods that distract us from the ultimate good. But sin is not the necessary outcome of free will. Sin is unnecessary if we cooperate with the Spirit of God at work in us.

Irenaeus held that we are personally responsible for our choices, whether virtuous or sinful, as we struggle to gain likeness to God. But his emphasis is on God's intention in creating humans. The intention of the creator was to bring us to divine *likeness* through our struggle to cooperate with the working of the Spirit in us. This Spirit is the power by which God raised Jesus from the dead, and so the working of the Spirit in us is the power of the death and resurrection

---

102. Russell, 232, quoting Frederick Schleiermacher, <u>The Christian Faith</u>.
103. Romans 8:6 and 9.

115

of Christ. The perspective of Irenaeus has room for the evolutionary journey of the human species into the future. Over the millennia, we have evolved with animal passions, self-reflective consciousness, intellect, free will, and the trait for religious thinking. Our struggle is to integrate these powers in our pursuit of the numinous, in pursuit of divinity.

God takes the greater responsibility to see to it that the divine plan for our transcendence is accomplished, and we have the responsibility to make virtuous choices toward that fulfillment. Our ongoing journey is also intimately tied to the journey of the whole of creation. Our humanity is one part of the whole Cosmos moving toward fulfillment. As one part transcends, the whole is affected and moves toward its fulfillment. Here we begin to understand that freedom of will is more than our ability to choose among alternative goods. True freedom of will is the ability consistently to choose what will move the whole to which we belong toward that fulfillment for which we were created, likeness to God.

As should be evident from our brief consideration of Irenaeus, Eastern Christianity does not have a developed theology of original sin. Instead, it developed a theology of our humanity and its divinization by the Holy Spirit, *theosis* in Greek. Divinization is a way of explaining God's intent from the beginning for the transcendence of the universe, which is now revealed in the person of Jesus the Christ. This divinization is not limited to human persons but is the work of the Spirit of God within all creation. However, the theology of divinization is dependent on a theological understanding of our humanity. We were created by God's Word and Spirit to be capable of becoming God in a human way. As such, we live in the world as the Cosmos responding to that capacity, which will be fulfilled in us through Christ and the power of his Spirit, for the sake of all creation.

This theology of divinization is compatible with a reinterpretation of Genesis that follows in the next chapter. We hold that sin is our continued immature human response to the phenomena of death, the full manifestation of all our other vulnerabilities in this material existence. The remedy for sin is a fuller response to God, animated in us by the Spirit. Our response to God begins with our conscious recognition of the numinous in the Cosmos. That numinous is God's first self-revelation. The death and resurrection of Christ is the completion of that first revelation. His resurrection is also the beginning of the fulfillment of creation as a whole, which was made possible by his corporate unity as a human with the whole of the material world.

The numinous in creation and in the person of Jesus allures us to seek the fullness of beauty, goodness, and truth which is God. In our restlessness to do so, we will ultimately find our fullness of life in God through Jesus Christ who is the enfleshment of God's Word by through whom all things were made. In his *Confessions*, Augustine offered some salient advice in this regard. Our hearts are made for union with God and restless until they rest in God. So too, the whole of the Cosmos is filled with a restlessness seeking something more, fulfillment through the Word by which it was made.

The Context for Reinterpreting Sin

The empirical evidence is that we humans evolved from other species on Earth, species whose suffering and death allowed for our emergence. For instance, it was the extinction of the dinosaurs that made room for our mammalian ancestors to proliferate. Theological explanations for suffering and death, if not rooted in this empirical evidence of evolution, will appear to be irrational explanations or novel fiction. For that reason, our reinterpretation of the myth of the original sin of Adam and Eve must be rooted in the scientific evidence that the presence of death on Earth preceded human evolution.

But our reinterpretation must also be rooted in the numinous, as well. The numinous is the source of our theological insight that creation exists because God desired to share existence. Through

117

Jesus the Christ, Christians believe, we can see it was the intent of the creator to share the fullness of existence, which is divine being, with creatures whose being was created contingent, subject to death. The being of God is the fullness of life. Through Jesus the Christ we have come to understand that it was not the intention of the creator that creation would lose its gift of existence through death but instead find its fulfillment in God, that is in *divinization.*

In the Genesis stories of creation, God creates humans in the divine image, inviting them to be partners in life, a relational way of being through which humans may manifest their likeness to God. While God always exceeds creation, this partnership with and sharing of God's way of existing is something for which humans were created. We evolved to be relational beings. When we sinned, God did not withdraw the invitation of relationship but opened a path through our sinfulness to fullness of life. Ancient Judeo-Christian wisdom declares that God does not desire the death of a sinner but rather our fullness of life. In the next chapter we will see how the fullness of life comes through death, emerges from cataclysm.

For now, we need to reaffirm the following ways of proceeding.

1) The Genesis myth of creation does not require us to believe nature was complete, perfect, or deathless at its beginning. We have empirical evidence that all lifeforms were from the beginning of creation subject to death. Original sin did not bring death into existence.

2) Our reinterpretation of original sin understands that sin occurred as *Homo sapiens* evolved a new trait, the trait for religious thinking with which they were able to recognize the numinous in creation. Our ability to perceive the numinous provided further development of our inherited trait for moral thinking which had simply sought the physical goods needed by our group. Religious thinking provided alternative options to our animal-striving to protect ourselves from our vulnerabilities in life and especially from death.

118

3) The trait for religious thinking is an example of what Brian Swimme calls the power of allurement which is pulsing through the Cosmos and each of us. As a result of religious thinking, all human cultures across time were built on varied responses to the human desire in the face of death to achieve a fuller life.

4) From the Christian perspective, the creator-God has been mentoring the human race across the millennia, drawing us in various ways through creation itself, to know and respond to God. Through the Jewish people God made clear, by giving us commandments, that we sin by choosing our own welfare over that of the whole to which we belong. Through the person of Jesus of Nazareth, God has fulfilled the creative plan for us and that same whole. His Spirit is given to us so that we can lead creation to its promised fulfillment by the way we live in communion with each other, with all life-forms and Earth itself.

Death and Human Cultures

In 1965, John Dunne, a Holy Cross priest, published his masterful work on human cultures, The City of God: A study in myth and mortality.[104] He described how each human culture across time has been built on that culture's mythic response to our human consciousness of death. Modern cultures, he explained, tend to think a myth is the way people thought in some past age. Dunne pointed out that every period has its myth, its story that guides its decisions on how to stave off vulnerabilities, especially death. For humans, the leading edge of our experience is constantly changing like a wave front. Cultures in each age readjust themselves to meet these changes. Our contemporary response to the question, "what can I do to satisfy my desire to live," becomes the normative standing point of the wave of our experience.

---

104. John Dunne, C.S.C., The City of God: A study of myth and mortality (NY: Macmillan Co., 1965).

119

For instance, we develop faster military responses to perceived threats or increase benefits to stabilize family life. The measures we take in riding the wave of our experience become the myth of our epoch. Lower taxes mean more money to invest in infrastructure, or increased immigration supplies needed workers. So, modern society's answer to the perennial question, "If I must die today, what can I do to satisfy my desire to live," will be considered the myth of the present age for those who come after us.[105]

Dunne shows that in each cultural epoch "the problem of death takes characteristic form and receives a characteristic solution."[106] A culture's characteristic solution pervades every aspect of that culture. For instance, it is a myth that nationalism stabilizes cultures, or conversely internationalism enriches cultures. Or think of contemporary political cultures taking measures to assure the care of citizens and deciding who holds the responsibility for that care. These measures are a culture's mythic response to the question of how to satisfy our desire to live in the face of death's certainty. A culture's basic myth is evident in its military and economic decisions and in how much autonomy can be tolerated among the citizenry before its leadership feels threatened.

At the same time, differing myths, old and new, may be simultaneously active within a given society because it is composed of differing cultures. This becomes evident in the face of a pandemic. Based on their controlling cultural myth, some will choose to be vaccinated and others not. Some want a government to assist in controlling the spread of a disease, and others forcefully reject its interventions. At the same time, in the evolution of human cultures, people continue to draw on ancient myths retold in new circumstances. The new circumstances prompt the myths and choices based on them to further evolve. As an example, some members of a society wonder if it is moral to receive a vaccination

---

105. Ibid., v.
106. Ibid., vii.

developed by using tissue from aborted human fetuses harvested decades before the pandemic and the development of a vaccine. Death, and the many human vulnerabilities it symbolizes, motivate many and varied choices.

Death and Wisdom Traditions

Human beings are not always consciously aware of their motivations, but when consciously aware of death's reality, we have come up with some very creative religious thinking about how to satisfy our desire to live. The Vedas, the canonical texts of Hinduism, are at least 5,000 years old, dating from around 3000 B.C.E. or even earlier. In Hinduism, the Supreme Soul or life-force is broken into parts or souls which enter matter as a living sentient being. After death, the soul of every creature is reborn repeatedly into the material world until that soul-life finally and fully reflects the goodness of the Supreme Soul and can reenter into union with it.

As long as a living creature is caught in the cycles of rebirth, death will recur repeatedly. Death in the Vedas becomes a symbol of all the inescapable suffering that inevitably affects all sentient life. In Vedic teaching, God is "The One" who is in all, and all are in "The One." In the popular mind this is pantheism, God and the Cosmos are one. But in fact, it is a form of panentheism, everything having its existence in God. In this form of panentheism, The One both permeates the Cosmos and transcends the Cosmos. As such, The One is both the cause of death and its remedy. The remedy which The One provides for a life-soul to escape the cycles of death and rebirth is right living, which releases the soul-life into The One.

A different response to the mystery of death is found in mummification which has been practiced in various cultures around the world. It was practiced in the Andes from as early as seven thousand years ago to as recently as 500 years. The bodies of very young virginal girls, who were purposely killed, were left in the mountains as offerings to the gods for the sake of the welfare of the tribe. They became naturally mummified by the weather in the mountainous terrain.

Perhaps the best-known practice of chemical mummification began in Egypt as early as 4500 B.C.E. The oldest funerary texts, the Pyramid Texts, date from 2400 to 2300 B.C.E. and originally were reserved for use when burying a Pharaoh. These Texts were originally preserved only as carvings within a Pharaonic tomb. In much later periods of Egyptian history, other persons of lower rank were included in this ritual to free the multiple life-forces to reunite beyond the tomb. The Pyramid Texts foreshadow in some ways the current cosmological theory that spirit within matter moves the material world toward an ultimate hoped-for transcendence.

The human traits for religious thinking and moral thinking are operative in these diverse practices. Right living as a remedy for the cycles of death and rebirth and the mummification of members to ensure the welfare of an individual or of an entire tribe are examples of moral thinking. Religious thinking seeks a return to the greater whole, or participation in the life of the gods, or gifting the gods with virginal human life to secure a fuller life for the tribe. The interplay between moral and religious thinking is also evident in the burial rituals of a Pharaoh. If the Pharaoh was to have hope of passing through the world of the dead to find new life, his heart when weighed by the gods had to be as light as a feather.

Great stone monuments were built in Neolithic Europe and across many other regions of the world. These structures symbolized both astronomical knowledge of the heavens and the possible ultimate transcendence of life. Monumental structures like Stonehenge in England celebrate both the oneness of the seasons and of Earth with the sun, while also symbolizing the hope of human transcendence in the face of death. Stonehenge, a marvel of construction, depends on mathematical and technical abilities hard for post-moderns to imagine the ancients possessing. Yet, these kinds of Neolithic structures were spread as far east as present-day Israel.

Stonehenge was built in six stages from around 3000 to 1520 B.C.E., during the Neolithic through Early Bronze Ages. It points toward the agricultural seasons and Earth's unique engagement with the sun that causes the seasons. Ancient observation recognized that the Sun's movement to the north signaled spring with its increase of light and consequent new growth on Earth. Science now shows that, as it revolves around the sun, it is Earth's tilt that causes the change of seasons.

Stonehenge also provided a place to celebrate the mystery of death. Passing into the darkness of death, those buried at the monument were offered the hope of transcendence as the light of the sun illumined the burial chambers at the spring equinox. Thus, the monument expressed religious thinking, that death itself pointed to transcendence, as do the seasons in their rhythm with the sun. Throughout the history of *Homo sapiens*, ancient structures and burials, funeral texts and stories about heroes and gods all sought to penetrate death's mystery and its relationship to some ultimate transcendence.

The Gilgamesh epic poem which dates from around 2100 B.C.E. in Mesopotamia is such a heroic tale and the starting point for Dunne's book on myth and mortality. Dunne describes Gilgamesh, the epic's protagonist, as "a man who went searching for the means to indefinitely prolong life."[107] As such, he says Gilgamesh is both more archetypal than later literary heroes and yet, like all human beings, a failure at his quest. The latter point is made clear by an extant tablet which describes how Gilgamesh lost the tree of life to a cunning snake, thus condemning all humankind to unending death. Another tablet explains how death entered the world. It records a conversation between Siduri, a barmaid, and the hero Gilgamesh. She tells him that when the gods created humankind, they gave us death and withheld eternal life for themselves. This ancient myth was later

---

107. Ibid., vi.

reworked within the Jewish culture to create the Genesis story of the original sin.

Conclusion

The information in this chapter is a necessary introduction to our reinterpretation of the third chapter of Genesis which follows We have set the context for a close look at that text of Genesis. This close look will help explain why a reinterpretation of the text is necessary. Our reinterpretation in turn will have a profound effect on our views concerning the definition of original sin, moral evil, redemption, and the intention of the creator for the fulfillment of creation.

Chapter VIII

Reinterpreting Original Sin

Rereading Genesis 3

The myth of original sin in Genesis was an attempt to account for moral evil and death in the world. The final editing of Genesis took place while the Jewish nation was in Babylonian exile around 538 B.C.E. The third chapter speaks in mythic language of a human choice that allowed death to influence the entirety of human experience. It tells us that,

> The LORD God gave man [Adam who stands for all humankind] this order: 'You are free to eat from any of the trees of the garden except the tree of knowledge of good and bad. From that tree you shall not eat; the moment you eat from it you are surely doomed to die'.[108]

Most readers understand that Adam and Eve ate. As a result, the normative interpretation tells us, they and their descendants were punished with death, moral disorder in themselves, and natural disorder in creation. But was that the editors' purpose in telling the myth, simply to explain how death and disorder entered creation? It does not appear so.

The editors' purpose in Genesis 3 is to encourage a religious life of faithfulness to God's commandments, which is what post-exilic Judaism strove to do in its religious practice after the return from Babylon in 607 B.C.E. In a Good Friday sermon, Terrance Klein, a Catholic priest and author of *Vanity Faith*, explained the relationship between being created and being faithful to God's commandments.

---

108. Genesis 2:16-17.

Klein says,

> In creating us, God fashioned a will and a freedom that stand apart
> from God's own self. This was the great adventure: to create that
> which could be called into God's life of love. But you cannot call
> others into love without granting them the possibility of rejecting
> it. One could say—and history, both human and environmental,
> bears this out—that God puts all of creation at risk in creating us,
> fashioning the one part of creation that can and did reject God.[109]

In Genesis, freedom of will is the ability to make a free, personal,
conscious, and active response to God's love. For *Homo sapiens*, our
free will is inherently linked to the possibility of rejecting the creator's
loving invitation to a relationship of shared life and the work of
caring for Earth and its life-forms. The current challenge is to explain
free will in the context of evolutionary cosmology rather than in the
fixed, completed cosmology in which the myth was originally
interpreted. To accomplish this challenge, we first must attend to the
details of the myth through the close reading that follows.

The myth of the Fall occurs in the Garden of Eden (Earth with
its abundance of life) which was created to be the dwelling place of
Adam and Eve. The story of original sin begins with a conversation
between a snake and Eve, the mother of humankind, about a
command of God that had accompanied the creation of Eden.

> Now the snake was the most cunning of all the wild animals that
> the LORD God had made. He asked the woman, 'Did God really
> say, you shall not eat from any of the trees in the garden?' The
> woman answered the snake: 'We may eat of the fruit of the trees
> in the garden; it is only about the fruit of the tree in the middle of
> the garden that God said, 'You shall not eat it or even touch it, or

---

109. Terrance W. Klein, <u>Vanity Faith: Searching for Spirituality among the Stars</u>,
(Collegeville, MN: Liturgical Press 2009). Accessed 4/2/2021 at
https://www.americamagazine.org/faith/2021/03/31/scripture-reflection-
catholic-good-friday-homily-lent-240359.

else you will die.' But the snake said to the woman: 'You certainly will not die! God knows well that when you eat of it your eyes will be opened and you will be like gods, who know good and evil'.[110]

The normative interpretation, with which we are most familiar, presumed Eden was a preternaturally peaceful existence which was disordered by the sin of Adam and Eve. According to that interpretation, Eden was deathless before sin. Nonetheless, Satan was an inexplicable evil presence disguised as a snake. Ironically, an evil presence would mean Eden was not a perfectly peaceful existence, because there is already temptation and a creature who leads Eve to break God's commandment. Nor is Eden completely deathless because there is the threat of death placed by the creator for breaking a divine commandment. Her conversation with the snake reminds Eve of the threat of death enshrined in God's commandment not to eat of the tree in the middle of the garden. And in that conversation, there is only one tree in the middle of the Garden, which is not named. We will examine all these features of the myth in this chapter.

As the story continues, Eve struggles with the decision whether to eat what appears delightful to her eyes but which she is commanded not to eat. Here is the description of free will subject to temptation, even before any sin is committed. But to be clear, the temptation is to attain a new knowledge, a knowledge of good and evil which would in some way make her like God. Her alternative in the myth is to obey a commandment of God. That command is meant to preserve God's intent for her to have life to the full by her faithfulness to a commandment.

The Jewish editors of the story were members of a covenanted people, a faith and culture rooted in finding the fullness of life through the fulfillment of divine commandments. They would have found it necessary for God to provide a commandment to guide the

---

110. Genesis 3:1-5.

choice of our first parents. A command gives knowledge concerning the value of an act. It would seem unjust for God to impose death without warning Adam and Eve of the consequence of their choice. Failure to observe a divine command is a sin, a rupture in the relationship with God, self, and others. But, more importantly, a commandment signals there is a relationship between the creator and humankind already in place. As we continue our close reading of the myth, we will consider whether a commandment was necessary, or whether the evolution of religious thinking, rather than a commandment, is what actually reshaped the relationship between humans and their creator.

The Snake

In truth, the idea of a Satan, the tempter, evolves in the Bible over time. Satan appears in the Book of Job as the State's prosecutor in the heavenly court. God permits Satan to try to entrap a good man into cursing God for the loss of his former pleasant way of life. By the time of the later Jewish prophets, around the return from the exile, Satan becomes what will later be encountered in the Gospels, a fallen angelic spirit who is the father of lies and prince of dark evils. Most readers, whether they are aware of its historical development or not, will be attuned to read that idea of Satan back into the original story in Genesis and so think of the snake as Satan.

But another detail in the myth gives a profound reason for readers doing so. The fact that the snake universalized the commandment "not to eat the fruit" by applying it to all the trees in the garden gives credence to the idea that the snake is Satan. The commandment was only about one tree in the middle of the garden, not all the trees. Temptation, if initially subtle, will show its intent to entrap when it is overblown. It is, therefore, understandable a religious reader would interpret the snake, for overplaying its hand, as Satan.

The snake in the original myth, however, was just a snake, and the myth identifies it was the most cunning of creatures. The snake as such represents moral thinking, how to achieve the greatest good for ourself and our group. The kind of thinking which Rappaport and Corbally say existed among our hominin ancestors before we developed the trait for religious thinking. Moral thinking motivates Eve to gather fruit to share with her mate. The snake suggests the fruit is good for something more, and God has kept this something more hidden from Eve and her mate. "God knows well that the moment you eat of it your eyes will be opened and you will be like gods who know what is good and what is bad."[111]

It was then that Eve saw the tree was not only good for food but pleasing to the eyes, and "desirable for gaining wisdom." But this kind of wisdom is cunning wisdom, a willfulness that makes self-interest the full measure of both good and evil. It also makes God out to be unwilling to share the fullness of life, as in the Gilgamesh myth. Eve, in turn, seeks to grasp that fullness of life by her own means, eating the fruit and sharing it with Adam.

Eve's decision to eat the fruit of the tree in the middle of the garden is an example of what Orthodox Christianity calls exercising a *gnomic* will. That means making a choice based on an opinion, or intention, or inclination, rather than on one's relationship with God. She is using the moral thinking of caring for her own interests. It is a choice motivated by desire but made with cunning, rather than truly understanding oneself as being-in-relationship with the whole of creation and with the creator.[112]

Eve's action lacked the simplicity of a dove, the symbol of the beloved. Jesus advised his disciples to have the simplicity of a dove and the cunning of a serpent when dealing with the world. It was good advice. Simplicity is knowing in truth to whom one belongs, and cunning is the necessary determination to achieve a goal. Ignore simplicity and cunning begets abuse; ignore determination and simplicity begets failure to act.

---

111. Genesis 3:5.
112. Andrew Louth, <u>Maximus the Confessor</u> (NY: Routledge, 1996), 59-62.

In the myth, simplicity for Eve would have been humbly following God's command as the true path to fulfillment. Hence, the need for a commandment to clarify God's intent to support her in her decision to choose the path to life, not death. [113] Instead, the woman listened to the snake's advice and exercised a *gnomic* will to power.

The Tree

Now we examine what tree the snake and Eve were discussing. There is some confusion here. In the story, the Tree of Life is said to be in the middle of the garden along with the tree of the knowledge of good and bad. But in the crucial moment of Eve's decision, there is but one tree in the middle of the garden which is not named. Is the Tree of Life also the Tree of the knowledge of good and bad? The woman says, "We may eat of the fruit of the trees in the garden; it is only about the fruit of the tree in the middle of the garden that God said, 'You shall not eat it or even touch it, or else you will die'."[114] Why is there only one tree mentioned here?

The creation myth says, "Out of the ground the LORD God made grow every tree that was delightful to look at and good for food, with the tree of life in the middle of the garden *and the tree of the knowledge of good and bad.*"[115] Later in the story, Adam and Eve are told, "You are free to eat from any of the trees of the garden except the tree of knowledge of good and bad. From that tree you shall not eat; the moment you eat from it you are surely doomed to die."[116] Does that mean they were free to eat of the other tree, the Tree of Life? That does not seem to be the case, because after the sin of Adam and Eve, "the LORD God said: 'See! The man has become like one of

---

113. Deuteronomy 30:19-20. "I call heaven and earth today to witness against you: I have set before you life and death, the blessing and the curse. Choose life, then, that you and your descendants may live, by loving the LORD, your God, heeding his voice, and holding fast to him."
114. Genesis 3:1-5.
115. Genesis 2:9, emphasis added.
116. Genesis 2:17-18.

us, knowing what is good and what is bad! Therefore, *he must not be allowed to put out his hand to take fruit from the tree of life also, and thus eat of it and live forever'.*"[117]

In various myths and world religions from India, through Asia and Europe, and even among Native Americans, a Tree of Life, World Tree, or Cosmic Tree is prominently featured. It has different functions in these myths. It holds together the Cosmos, or maintains the separation of the sky and land, and/or brings forth the gifts of life. In Egypt and Mesopotamia, the Tree of Life is associated with a fig tree which can grow in a desert oasis; it brings forth nourishing fruit and indicates the location of lifesaving water.

In later Judaism, the Tree of Life was equated with the Law of God (Torah) and with the Wisdom of God, as in Proverbs 3:18, "She is a tree of life to those who grasp her, and he is happy who holds her fast." Can the Wisdom of God be the Tree of Life and at the same time be the source of suffering and death? It could be a second tree, the tree of the knowledge of good and evil, was added later to the story to protect the Tree of Life, and by extension the Creator, from the accusation of creating a universe which causes suffering and death.

The Jewish belief is that the Creator desires life to flourish for all creatures.[118] Separating the tree of the knowledge of good and evil from the Tree of Life could be a necessary editorial development. The separate identities of the two trees would make clear that the Creator's intent in the act of creating was to give life, not death. At the same time, it portrays the Jewish sentiment that the punishment to follow is for breaking a commandment. Thus, it shows the need for commandments that will guide human free will away from sin and punishment and toward likeness with God's design for the life of the

---

117. Genesis 3:22-23, emphasis added.
118. Later Jewish texts, cf. Wisdom 1:12-14, state that it was not God who created death but death entered the world through the envy of the devil. Ezekiel 18:32 and 33:11 state that God takes no pleasure in the death of a sinner but wants the sinner to return God and have life.

world. Living according to the commandments fosters life, breaking them increases the inevitable power of death in the world.

But can the Tree of Life also be the source of the knowledge of good and bad, of both life and of death? From an evolutionary point of view, there is only one tree needed, the Tree of Life. During the evolution of our species and during the human development of any individual person, life itself teaches us that we must deal both with goods and their losses. In the evolution of our species, we responded to these experiences by evolving traits for both moral and religious thinking.

Moral thinking motivated choices of goods that benefit myself and my group. Religious thinking motivated us to expand our moral choices so that we could choose life to the full for ourselves, all living creatures, and Earth to which we belong. Religious thinking, through the hope of transcendence generated by the numinous, even extended the possibility of life for us beyond our time-limited life on Earth. In reinterpreting the myth of the original sin, I think we can say the trait for religious thinking made Eve aware of a relationship with the creator. It was in relation to God she would make her decision. But what was the decision?

Original Sin in Context

Eve's dilemma about eating the fruit of the tree in the middle of the garden is a Gilgamesh-like moment. Gilgamesh, the hero of a pre-Genesis myth, wanted to avoid death and attain the extension of his life. His assurance of the extension of his life was the possession of the Tree of Life which eventually was stolen from him by a snake. Lacking the assurance of eternal life that the tree would have provided, Gilgamesh was advised to simply enjoy the good things of life as a distraction from the inevitability of death.

Eve's situation, between the threat of death and the seeking of wisdom, is the symbol of an emergent moment of human consciousness. Here is the emergence of religious thinking in a world where everything eventually dies. In the face of the threat of death, making our self-interests the measure of moral good and evil, without reference to the greater whole to which we belong, is the essence of the original sin which has been handed down through the generations and repeated by each human person.

In the Genesis myth of the fall, Eve is confronted by the threat of personal death in the same moment she becomes aware of the numinous. The numinous is represented by the fruit that is pleasing to the eye and good for obtaining wisdom. Awareness of the numinous is the possibility of the knowledge of the goodness of life, a knowledge that the creator has because God is the full measure of goodness. The threat of death is meant to keep her from setting herself and her interests as the measure of good and evil in the world. Her choice to eat the fruit of the tree is a choice to measure the good of life according to her own interests alone. But tragically, by making the choice to measure the good in life according to her own self-interest, she and her descendants are confronted with their inability as creatures to avoid death. Death impresses itself upon human consciousness *in a new way* through this missing the mark of who we are and of what we are a part.

About 300,000 years ago, our *Homo sapiens* ancestors were presented with just such a dilemma. Because of the evolution of the trait for religious thinking, they became aware of the personal nature of death in the same moment they became aware of the numinous in their own existence. Both the good which is life and the deprivation of that good, called death, became a part of our religious thinking. Our struggle ever since, as we make decisions about our relationship to the greater whole opened for us by the numinous, has been between two alternatives. We can make our choices based on our immediate self-interest and try to extend our life by our own efforts. Alternatively, we can exercise our trait for religious thinking in making our decisions for the good of the whole to which we belong. The questions are simple ones. Do we grab what we can, for we may soon die? Or, as we use the goods of creation, do we love our neighbor as ourselves and do to others as we would have them do to us?

In the Genesis myth, Eve and her husband, Adam, join in making a choice for self-interest over their relationship with the creator, the source of every good.[119] Adam and Eve seek to be like God by making their self-interest the measure of life's beauty, goodness, and truth. It is rather clear from our historic experience that from the beginning we *Homo sapiens* have been using this same measure. In the history of humankind, the extension of our own lives by any means has continued to be the human measure for determining good and evil. This is an ongoing choice to be like God but by our own effort alone. This kind of cunning wisdom is not likeness to God, but what we have been calling a *gnomic* wisdom, human willfulness.[120] Its measure is simple. Since we personally will die, we use the goods of Earth to extend our life, despite the cost to each other, our fellow creatures, or to Earth itself.

Like our forbearers, we humans continue to distract ourselves by consuming the fruits of life in order to transcend life with its vulnerabilities and death. This is our shared sin in the face of the numinous. It is the pretense that the extension of our own lives is the sole measure by which to judge between good and evil in our dealing with Earth and its creatures. Here we see the consequences of the

---

119. There have been various interpretations of the detail that it is Eve who first recognized the fruit of the forbidden tree as delightful and in turn offered some to Adam. Some interpretations were very misogynistic. If we simply look to human socialization prior to the beginning of agriculture, men hunted and women gathered. Eve is gathering fruit in the garden and is doing so with diligence. In the myth, the decision to eat is a joint decision, which in part is why the original sin and it consequences have a corporate character.
120. Gerald May, M.D., Will and Spirit: A contemplative theology (NY: Harper Collins Publishers, 1982) gives a fuller understanding of the concept of willingness, a human will set truly free to pursue fullness of life, and willfulness, the tendency of the human will to become entrapped, seeking what is less than fullness of life.

original sin. Instead of acting as a being-in-relationship, we are pulled toward acting according to the instincts we share with our animal forebears, chief among which is self-preservation at the expense of others. Since the evolution of the trait for religious thinking, ancient wisdom traditions have been trying to teach us a different way of life.

Our evolved traits for self-reflection and religious thinking are examples of the wisdom of God at work in an evolving universe. The Book of Wisdom, part of the Jewish writings, offers a meditation on what happens when humans refuse to use these traits to seek the numinous. The book begins by saying God did not create death. However, the fuller context shows that God did not create death to be the end of life. Rather, those who trust themselves to God are alive even in death. Death is only permanent for those who place themselves in the power of death by using death as an instrument to gain power over others. By doing so, they oppose the wisdom of God in the order of creation and remain themselves in death's power.[121]

In this Jewish book, the wisdom of God is personified as female, much like the Greek *Sophia*. In Christian theology the Wisdom of God, which permeates all creation, is made flesh in the person of Jesus of Nazareth. Christians believe it is in him that the full wisdom of God concerning likeness to God is revealed. His death opens a pathway through death to transcendence, to resurrection and eternal life, to being like God, *divinization*. The material world is to find its completion by that same path, through the cataclysm of death, that leads to emergence into the glory of God.

The Consequences of Sin

In the Genesis myth of the Fall, after sharing the forbidden fruit,

> the eyes of both of them were opened, and they knew that they were naked; so they sewed fig leaves together and made loincloths for themselves. When they heard the sound of the LORD God

---

121. Wisdom 1:12—3:9.

walking about in the garden at the breezy time of the day, the man and the woman hid themselves from the LORD God among the trees of the garden. The LORD God then called to the man and asked him: 'Where are you?' He answered, 'I heard you in the garden; but I was afraid, because I was naked, so I hid.' Then God asked: 'Who told you that you were naked? Have you eaten from the tree of which I had forbidden you to eat?'[122]

Their nakedness which had been their natural state now has become the symbol of their folly, and to cover it they sew together fig leaves to make loincloths. The covering of their genitals is a symbol of sexual shame. What is the origin of sexual shame according to the myth? Eve and Adam were created to be suitable partners, not competitors, in life. Sexual shame comes from making oneself the measure of one's own fulfillment, instead of finding in the other one's true self. The pleasure of sexual orgasm, known in French as *le petite mort*, the little death, can seduce us into believing that sexual pleasure is our fulfillment, instead of the unity it can foster with each other.

Asked why he ate the fruit, the man says, "The woman whom you put here with me, she gave me fruit from the tree, so I ate it."[123] It is a double accusation, against God for providing her as his companion in life and against the woman who tempted him with the fruit. In a cunning manner, the man takes no personal responsibility for exercising his free will. Instead, his willfulness is manifest in blaming God and his other self, Eve. We seek intimacy but the path for that transformation, two becoming one flesh, is blocked by blaming and shaming each other.

The woman's defense is, "The snake tricked me, so I ate it."[124] Genesis points out that our cunning willfulness is expressed in the

---

122. Genesis 3:7-11.
123. Genesis 3:12.
124. Genesis 3:13.

human game of personal irresponsibility that leads us to blame and shame the rest of creation as well for thwarting our goals. We seek synergy, working together as one with Earth and its creatures, but our efforts are defeated by our own willful seeking of our individual interests.

To the woman God says, "I will intensify your toil in childbearing; in pain you shall bring forth children."[125] It sounds as if the pain of giving birth was already present in Eden, but now is intensified as a punishment for sin. Are we to understand the physical pain of childbirth is a punishment? Or is there another understanding that links childbearing's pain to our struggle to extend our lives by our own means?

Let us consider some reasons among humans for bearing children which themselves intensify the pain of childbirth. Some say they want a child to provide care for themselves in their aged vulnerability, while others want to prolong their existence after death through their children's lives. And yet, it is true that we give birth to our children knowing we cannot preserve ourselves or them from death. Still, because we are created in the image of God, we have the intense desire to share life, human existence, which is expressed in childbearing. That desire moves a woman to risk the physical pain and the danger of death that childbearing entails. In human wisdom traditions, the intense desire to share life is a taste of the numinous, of God drawing the world to the fullness of life which is yet beyond our horizon of knowing. But our inability to know the outcome of the choice we make to beget a child can be itself an intense pain.

At the same time, this very desire to share life is touched by sin. In the same verse, God also tells the woman, "Your urge shall be for your husband, and he shall rule over you."[126] The woman will desire sexual union for the begetting and rearing of children, but she will experience domination by the very partner with whom she seeks to

---

125. Genesis 3:16.
126. Genesis 3:16.

be a partner-in-being. As we said earlier, the domination of one sex by the other is not part of the plan of God. The lack of benevolent care among humans around sexual issues is clearly one of the consequences of original sin. Although sexism and every other form of sexual domination is contrary to the intent of the creator according to the myths of creation in Genesis, sexual domination continues in its many forms to be the evidence of sins against the dignity of others.

Genesis describes still another consequence of sin, that we are turned against Earth and Earth against us. Our decision to make ourselves the supreme measure of what is good on Earth is a decision whose overwhelming ecological consequences are now catastrophic. In the myth, God says to the man:

> Because you listened to your wife and ate from the tree about which I commanded you, 'you shall not eat from it,' cursed is the ground because of you! In toil you shall eat its yield all the days of your life. Thorns and thistles it shall bear for you, and you shall eat the grass of the field. By the sweat of your brow you shall eat bread, until you return to the ground, from which you were taken; for you are dust, and to dust you shall return.[127]

This passage has often been read as God's condemnation of humankind. Rather, it is God's acknowledgement of our on-going struggle to mature in our relationships with Earth and its creatures. This struggle has continued over three hundred thousand years, but it is a struggle in which we are not left alone by God.

God's Fidelity

According to the Greek version of Genesis, God stationed an angel with a fiery sword "to guard the way to the tree of life."[128] In the Hebrew version, this purposeful action on God's part is missing.

---

127. Genesis 3:17-19.
128. Genesis 3:24.

What the Greek version translates as a messenger or angel guarding the Tree of Life is simply a single word in Hebrew, "Cherubim." What is the difference? The difference is that the Greek version fosters the interpretation that the angel is guarding the Tree of Life *from* the humans. God is withholding the fullness of life from them because of their infidelity. The Hebrew version makes no such claim. The word Cherubim stands alone and is left to be interpreted.

According to some Rabbis, the Cherubim is there to lead the humans by a new path to the Tree of Life.[129] This alternative interpretation makes all the difference in understanding that, as God confirms the consequences of human willfulness, the Creator has not changed the divine will to bring humankind to life in abundance. God is single minded and invites us to be the same. Christians believe it was to provide us life in abundance that God sent a Savior and did not limit that promise of abundance of life only to *Homo sapiens*, as we shall see in the next chapter.

Before we move there, however, let us consider whether continuing to speak of human nature as fallen is appropriate in view of this chapter's reinterpretation of the Genesis myth. Creation did not come into existence as complete and finished, so there was no fall from a state of being which did not include sin or death. Did our human ancestors fall from a state of perfect relationship with the creator and all the other creatures? Not if we are willing to engage empirical evidence of the evolution of species which includes the death of previous hominin species but excludes the presence of

---

129. Christian theologians found evidence elsewhere in Greek version of the myth that God provided a remedy for sin and death. They interpreted God's conversation with the serpent as a promise to send a savior for fallen humanity, specifically by translating God's saying a descendent of Eve will crush the head of the serpent. Some interpreted it to be a new Eve who would crush the serpent's head, which led to Christian art presenting Mary, the mother of Jesus, as the new Eve with her foot on the head of the serpent.

religious thinking. But did death enter the world because of our ancestor's choice to disobey a divine commandment? Death did not enter the world because of our failure to observe a commandment. Entropy was part of material creation from the beginning, as was natural death, entropy's consequence for all life-forms.

However, the consciousness of our personal vulnerabilities and especially of our personal death did come into existence with religious thinking, and that consciousness has motivated our decisions to sin. We are at times consciously aware of this motivation, but more frequently, it unconsciously affects our decisions. That is why moral theology speaks about different degrees of seriousness of sin and of culpability for our decisions. However, as Rene Girard shows in his writing about victimization, death is the weapon of preference we use to achieve our own self-interests. This is born out in the fourth chapter of Genesis. Following the story of the original sin, Cain, the son of Adam and Eve, exercises a cunning willfulness and kills his brother, Abel.

Death is the human instrument for power over others through random victimization in every human society, by various forms of domination in economic, political, or personal relationships, by the decision that another person's life has lesser value, or by the decision that one's own life is not worth living, which even motivates some to suicide.[130] Using death to achieve some purpose in our human

---

130. Suicide is an instrumental use of death that, relatively recently in our culture, has received a degree of compassion previously unusual in western societies. This is because of the data offered in psychological research that the person who suicides is most probably suffering overwhelming distress and agony, induced by depression or from some other neurologically compromising condition. In some ancient cultures (e.g. Roman and Japanese) suicide was accepted as a dignified release from situations that compromised a person's social dignity, for instance the loss of political stature. In our contemporary culture, medically assisted suicide has been proposed for similar losses of dignity due to medical conditions. In each of these instances, however, death remains an instrument to achieve an individual's desired termination but with questionable consideration of the entirety of the whole to which the person belongs.

relationships appears to be, at least in part, an inheritance from our evolution from other life-forms. However, it is essential to note that we also inherited from these ancestral life-forms the tendency to share life with others. These two tendencies continue to be in conflict in each human person and in all our human societies, even as religious thinking offers to reconcile them in seeking the common good.

In our evolution from unreflective animal to self-reflecting human, the instrumentalization of death in the pursuit of our self-interests is clearly contrary to the intent of the creator. Our trait for religious thinking which recognizes the numinous in creation indicates a different intent on the part of the creator. How we decide to deal with entropy and death either ignores or embraces the allure of life in abundance offered by the numinous, which is ultimately the allure of God. We have not fallen from an original innocence that can be described as being without sin. But we have been struggling from our evolution as *Homo sapiens* to mature into divine likeness, a divine dream made evident in Jesus the Christ. We struggle to transform ourselves from our default setting, which is making ourselves the center of our isolated universe of self-preservation. But that is not possible for us alone to accomplish. The original sin, which has influenced all human behaviors across the ages and is repeated by each person in our individual lives, is to refuse transcendence into union with the whole to which we belong. And since that whole includes the creator whose plan was to draw us by Word and Spirit into the divine likeness, all sin is a rupture in our relationship with God.

Conclusion

The two Genesis myths of creation offer us a developed understanding of the relationship between the creator-God and creation. God shares being, engenders relationships, draws and mentors humankind to divine likeness as we continue to evolve. In

141

these myths, the Creator invites human beings into an I-Thou relationship, as a new creature who has the trait for seeking the numinous, for seeking God.

The myth of original sin renders human evolution itself a story of the creator calling humankind toward a future of fulfillment, in likeness of being. Missing the mark, or sin, is inevitable as we struggle to respond to this call to likeness of being with God, but sin is not necessary. Sin is inevitable because we have free will, and we struggle in our relationships to be truly free because of our willfulness. But sin is not the necessary outcome of free will. Sin is unnecessary if we cooperate with the Spirit of God in our decisions. Such a response of *Homo sapiens* to the numinous, God's self-revelation in the created world, promises benefits for the whole Earth, sharing the benevolent care of the creator with all of creation.

The Genesis myth of original sin reminds us that from the beginning we have struggled against our innate tendency to measure our welfare solely according to our personal passions, "to do it my way." The myth expresses a truth, that we are called instead to walk the numinous path to a new evolutionary consciousness. This consciousness, as described by Genesis, is the deepening consciousness of our interrelatedness with creation and with its creator. That kind of synergy within nature offers a passionate way of living life to the full.

It may be possible, as Dunne suggests at the end of his book on myth and mortality in human cultural evolution, that humankind could deal differently with death to bring about the fullness of life for themselves and all life-forms.[131] That was the vision Teilhard de Chardin claimed a century ago in his Mass on the World in which the whole of creation is consecrated as an offering made in union with Christ's offering of himself on the cross. In the next chapters, we will examine Teilhard's vision in which, at the heart of

---

131. Dunne, 231.

the Cosmos, there is place for Jesus the Christ who opened a path through death to life in abundance.

Chapter IX

The Heart of Matter

The Cosmos in a Piece of Bread

A boy dropped his piece of bread on the floor. His Italian grandmother encouraged him to pick it up and kiss the piece of bread before eating it. The reason for the kiss she said, "Jesus is in the bread." The boy picked up the bread, kissed it, and began to eat it. He grew up to be the rector of a Catholic theological seminary where he recalled this childhood memory in a lecture on sacramental theology.

His topic that day was the doctrine that the bread and wine received during the Liturgy of the Eucharist is truly the body and blood of Jesus the Christ. His memory was an example of contextual thinking which he used to explain the theology of the Eucharist. What appeared only as bread fallen on the floor was, as the boy consumed it, something much more. Through the bread, he experienced an encounter with his grandmother, with the presence of Jesus in whom both believed, and with a transcendent vision of the material world. All this became the substance of the bread as he kissed and ate it. In this chapter, we will consider how the Liturgy of the Eucharist is for believers the encounter with the person of Jesus the Christ at the heart of the Cosmos.

Not all the world believes in Jesus the Christ, but everyone in the world gets hungry. Thich Nhat Hanh, a Buddhist monk, described the mindful eating of bread as a cosmic liturgy.

> Look deeply and you notice the sunshine in the bread, the blue sky in the bread, the cloud and the great earth in the bread. Can you tell me what is not in a piece of bread? The whole cosmos has come together in order to bring to you this piece of bread. You eat it in such a way that you come alive, truly alive.[132]

The whole Cosmos coming together to bring us the bread we eat is an experience of its seamless generativity. For the boy's grandmother, the source of cosmic seamlessness was Jesus the Christ. Presumably, she had never heard of Pierre Teilhard de Chardin (1881-1955), the French Jesuit priest and paleontologist, whose writings on the Cosmic Christ were published posthumously. Nevertheless, from her sharing the bread in the Catholic Liturgy of the Eucharist, she had encountered the person of Jesus at the heart of matter.

Eucharist in the Christian Scriptures

Luke, Matthew, and Mark report the words Jesus spoke at a Passover supper with his disciples. Before his passover on the cross, he gave them bread saying this is my body and a cup of wine saying this is my blood. In early Christian churches, where the Gospels writers lived, the presence of the risen Christ had been celebrated as

---

132. Thich Nhat Hanh, Going Home: Jesus and Buddha as Brothers (NY: Riverhead Books, 1999), 107.

Eucharist, Greek for *thanksgiving,* for two generations. Luke, at the end of his gospel, presents that thanksgiving liturgy as it was celebrated in his local church. The theme of journey is prevalent throughout his Gospel. So, Luke places the celebration of the Eucharist within the story of a journey of faith on the very day of Christ's resurrection. The story takes place on the road from Jerusalem to Emmaus. Christ makes his risen presence known to two of his disciples by first sharing the scriptures that prophesied his death and then sharing bread with them.

As the story unfolds, Jesus meets two disciples as they journey home from Jerusalem where his death occurred. They did not recognize him as he inquired about their conversation along the way. They were amazed this traveler did not know about the death of Jesus that took place recently. Disappointed by his death, they had hoped he was the Messiah. In response to their disappointment, Jesus explains the Jewish scriptural testimony that the Messiah had to suffer to enter his glory. His disciples could have found such explanations in the four songs of the suffering servant of God in the writings of Isaiah and in several of the psalms which speak of the sufferings of God's servants.[133] Only at the end of their journey when Jesus is invited to share a meal with them, does the risen Christ reveal himself to his disciples in the breaking of bread.

---

133. Isaiah 42:1 – 4; Isaiah 49 :1–6; Isaiah 50:4–11; and Isaiah 52:13 – 53:12, and Psalms 22 and 69.

Luke thus outlined how the Liturgy of the Eucharist was celebrated since the earliest times. The Liturgy of the Eucharist originated as a weekly gathering to celebrate the Lord's Day, the day of Christ's resurrection. The first half of the rite is the Liturgy of the Word, or public worship during which the voice of Christ is heard through the scriptures. This precedes the Liturgy of Eucharist in which Christ makes his presence known in a meal of bread and wine. This Sunday celebration nourished the community in its journey of faith in Christ from week to week until he comes again.

John the Apostle makes a similar point in his Gospel. He devotes the sixth chapter to an explanation that Christ is both God's Word to be heard and believed, so that believers might have life, and the Bread of Life, that when eaten in faith brings eternal life. That leaves John free during his last supper account to present lengthy prayers in which Jesus, for the sake of his disciples, consecrates himself by his death to God his Father. During these prayers, Jesus uses the analogy of a vine and its branches to describe his sharing life with the members of the community of believers, the church. He prays they may have the same relationship as he has with his Father. Christ the Vine, during the liturgy of Eucharist, shares his own fullness of life with the gathered community, so that they in turn can bring forth its fruits in their lives.[134] This sharing of life completes the joy of his interrelatedness with his disciples, while the fruits they bring forth

---

134. John 15.

give glory to God. Their lives are to be acts of Eucharistic thanksgiving in the midst of the world.

In these different ways, the four Gospels contextualize the faith and practice of the first Christian believers as a liturgy within a community at worship. Before the Gospel accounts of Christ's last supper were written down, the Apostle Paul had already described Christian faith in Christ's real presence as they celebrated the Liturgy of the Eucharist.[135] In his first letter, Paul refers to the practice at Corinth of celebrating that liturgy at the end of a larger community meal at which each family or social group ate the food they had prepared and brought with them. Only after their Agape (love) meal did they share the Eucharist.

Paul corrects the practice of the wealthier members of the community eating sumptuously while the poorer members have had less to eat. The reason for his rebuke is the words of Christ at his last supper, "this is my body...this is my blood." Christian faith in Christ's true presence as bread and wine should motivate a change in the way the rich members of a Christian community treat the poorer members. Eucharist was supposed to celebrate the common and equal share in Christ offered by the Spirit to each member in the community, which Paul referred to as Christ's Body. As Christ indwells each member, so each member indwells the others as one Body in Christ.

---

135. I Corinthians 11:23-26.

For Paul, the presence of Christ to the community in the celebration of the Eucharist was supposed to effect a transformation in the members, making them partners-in-being, whose corporate life as church makes Christ known to the world. Eating sumptuously while others had little or nothing contradicted the very action of Christ in the Eucharist, who gave all to each without distinction. Not recognizing the presence of Christ in the members of his body, the gathered church, was the same as not recognizing the presence of Christ in the sharing of his body and blood. Worse yet, it made one guilty of the death of the Lord, of being competitors like the religious and civil leaders who satisfied their own needs in crucifying Jesus.

Why did the first Christians believe so firmly that Christ was truly present under the symbols of bread and wine? They believed, as Paul taught at the beginning of the letter, that those baptized by water and the Spirit into Christ's death and resurrection were living a life of faith in which their substance was being changed into his likeness, humanity sharing divinity. They believed, as Paul also taught, that in the person of Christ Jesus they were encountering the foundation on which to build a life of unity with each other in likeness to God.

These beliefs were the context for Paul's interpretation of the words of Jesus at supper the night before he died. Jesus had said the bread he gave his disciples to eat was his body and the wine his blood. Paul declared that each time the members of the church shared this communion, they were declaring the power of Christ's self-emptying death until he came again in glory. Many contemporary Christians believe they participate in the same transcendent encounter with

Christ, as they pray during a Eucharistic liturgy for him to come again and fulfill the promised redemption of the whole Cosmos.

The Problem of Doctrine

Over the centuries, however, the Eucharist was de-contextualized. Instead of a liturgy, an action of the community joined with Christ in giving thanks to God, Eucharist became the name for the consecrated bread alone. This occurred gradually over several centuries but ultimately affected a division among Christians that still exists today. It began with the best of intentions. Some of the bread consecrated during a liturgy was taken to the sick and dying so that, although physically distant, they could share in the Eucharist as members of the community at worship. It gradually became the practice to reserve a portion of that consecrated bread at the place of the liturgy, the church building, so that it could be taken to the sick and especially to the dying in hope of resurrection, as Jesus promised in the Gospel according to John.

Gradually the reserved sacrament was given a place of honor in the church building and worshiped as the presence of Christ, but outside the liturgy from which it originated. The result of this liturgical de-contextualization was the growth of controversy over what appeared simply to be bread, the wine being consumed by the priests and not reserved for various practical reasons. Eucharist became a thing about which cognitive assertions were made in the form of doctrinal statements, instead of a liturgy in which the community was being transformed by the Spirit into the likeness of

Christ whom they heard, believed, and received in holy communion. Since the Second Vatican Council in the 1960s, multiple efforts have been made to recontextualize Eucharist within its liturgical and communal context.[136]

Doctrinal statements defining Christ's presence in the Eucharistic bread are intended to clarify what has been handed down since New Testament times. However, no doctrine stands by itself but is contingent on other teachings. For instance, what is the definition of church, of baptism, and of priesthood? These doctrines are assertions about how the Christian community understands its own practice of celebrating the Eucharist. To be rightly understood, these doctrines demand a contextual understanding of the Christian community in which such assertions are made. For that reason, the Roman Catholic

---

136. Since the Second Vatican Council, the Catholic Church has made multiple efforts to re-contextualize the adoration of the Blessed Sacrament with its liturgical context, the Mass or Liturgy of the Eucharist. Examples are 1) ending the practice of celebrating Mass before the exposed Blessed Sacrament, 2) requiring that there be no final blessing or dismissal if there is exposition at the end of Mass, 3) the portion of the sacrament exposed at the end of Mass should be taken from what was consecrated at that Mass, so that exposition of the Blessed Sacrament may be experienced as a continuation of the liturgy, 4) requiring scripture to be proclaimed at the beginning of exposition if it takes place apart from Mass, and 5) encouraging the faithful to participate fully in the Mass, including receiving Holy Communion frequently, especially at Sunday Mass. The Mass is a nickname for the Liturgy of the Eucharist and comes from a medieval Latin translation of the dismissal at the end of the liturgy. At that time, the congregations would hear the proclamation, "Ite, Missa est!" The Latin literally means, "Go, it is sent." However in Christian usage it gradually took on a deeper meaning. The word 'dismissal' has come to imply a 'mission.' These few words succinctly express the missionary nature of the Church (Benedict XVI, Sacramentum Caritatis, 51). Even the nickname, Mass, is contextual.

doctrine of the real presence demands the context of the liturgy, the community's worship of God.

The Church's doctrine states that during the Eucharistic prayer, the substance of the bread and wine becomes here and now the body and blood of the risen Christ, whose coming in glory will complete the Cosmos. The external characteristics (or species) of bread and wine, such as color and taste, remain so that it may be consumed by the faithful. But the change in the bread and wine to become Christ's body and blood is possible, according to Eastern Catholic or Byzantine theology, because of the Spirit, who is the power of Christ's resurrection that is shepherding the world to its completion. The Spirit, through the consecratory prayer of the community led by its priest, brings about this transformation of earthly elements, just as the Spirit overshadowed the Virgin Mary so that she could conceive the Word of God as Jesus of Nazareth.

It is also the doctrinal teaching of Roman Catholicism that, by the overshadowing of the Spirit's power, Christ's words, "Take and eat for this is my body…this is the chalice of my blood," uttered by a priest in the Eucharistic prayer, bring about the change in the bread and wine. That change is called "transubstantiation," which means what was bread and wine are now the body and blood of Christ.[137]

---

137. In Lutheran theology these words of Christ uttered at his last supper make his presence known in, with, through and under the signs of the bread and wine, so that Christ is truly present and received. But some reality of bread and wine also remain. Among Reformed Protestants, the doctrine is a bit different. Christ's body, after his resurrection and ascension to the right hand of God, is no longer available to us in this created order. The Holy Spirit, however, makes the risen Christ present to the church. The liturgy of the Eucharist is a remembrance of

In *The Mass on the World: a modern theory of transubstantiation*, Richard Pendergast, S.J., demonstrated how contemporary science can be the context for a more adequate understanding of transubstantiation for our time.[138] He says that in the natural cosmic hierarchy, lower elements are taken up into higher ones. Higher elements, like humans, cannot be reduced to the lower elements which compose them, like neurons or carbon. *Homo sapiens* are more than the inanimate compounds that compose us and the sensate life-forms from which we evolved. We have progressed even beyond the other species of hominins whose DNA are part of us.

It is possible, therefore, Pendergast concludes, that human nature could be taken up into a new way of being, as Christians believe Jesus of Nazareth was taken up by the Word of God from the flesh of a virgin. Likewise, Christians believe they are taken up in baptism to be sons and daughters of God, sharing the divinity of the Word who humbled himself to share our humanity. As the Word of God took up our humanity in the person of Jesus and takes believers by faith and baptism into his Body the Church, so also bread and wine may be taken up by the Word of God. That would mean what is present

---

Christ's redeeming work, during which the Spirit makes Christ's saving work present to the participants, in hope of resurrection and eternal life when he comes again. These theologies have in common that Christ's presence, as they celebrate the liturgy, affects the life of the church and the world. Their diverse explanations of how Christ's presence and its power is realized is the result of their diverse theologies of church and ministry (priesthood), as well as their diverse perspectives on the material world and God's interaction with its structure and contingencies.

138. Richard J. Pendergast, S.J., The Mass on the World: A modern theory of transubstantiation (NY: Herder & Herder, 2020), 11-15.

in species of bread and wine is in fact a higher presence, the presence of the body and blood of the risen Christ for the nourishment of his Body, the Church. The Community at prayer is the context for this change.

The Liturgy of the Eucharist is always the context in which to understand the Eucharistic presence of Christ. The Liturgy of the Eucharist enacts God's intention to bring creation to its fulfillment through Jesus the Christ. In union with the prayer of the presider, those present offer not just the bread and wine but themselves and the whole world to God as one sacrifice with Christ's. By the power of the Holy Spirit they seek to become truly Christ's presence both in the midst of the world and in the kingdom of heaven. They also pray that the world itself might be transformed in his likeness. The Eucharistic prayer led by the presider includes the offering of the whole world through the offering of body and blood of Christ to the creator.

In the communion rite of the Mass, the elements of bread and wine, now become the body and blood of Christ, are consumed as a meal which is truly a cosmic event. When consumed, the elements of bread and wine are broken open, a cataclysmic event, effecting the emergence of the risen Christ in those who eat and drink in faith. In this meal, Christ the head and those who are members of his corporate body, the Church, share one life with the creator-God and with all creation. Holy Communion, then, is a proleptic event. It is a taste of Cosmic fulfillment.

As the bread and wine are consumed with faith, the presence of the risen Christ brings about an experience of transcendence in and among those who consume these gifts. Those who receive communion have in the Eucharistic prayer offered themselves to God in, with, and through Jesus Christ and his sacrificial death. In return, by receiving communion, they become what they eat, share in his divine life. In the Liturgy of the Eucharist, Christ makes the community one with his risen self, through his presence as their Bread of Life and Cup of Salvation. This emergence of Christ in the faithful is in accord with the community's faith that Jesus the Christ is the source of the seamless generativity in the Cosmos and its promised fulfillment into which they were reborn by baptism.[139]

Teilhard de Chardin's Cosmic Liturgy

The Liturgy of the Eucharist, the Catholic Mass, is a public ritual in which billions of persons have participated over two millennia. The first chapter of Teilhard's book *Hymn of the Universe* is entitled "The Mass on the World." There he shares an expanded vision of

---

139. Colossians 1:16-17. The forgiveness of sins is a preparation for the divinization of those receiving communion and for the Cosmos' final divinization. The sacrament of Reconciliation is for the renewal of baptismal life in each sinful member of Christ's Body, the Church. For this reason, the discipline of celebrating another sacrament, Penance or Reconciliation, became an important preparation for receiving holy communion. In the Byzantine Rite, receiving Holy Communion is regarded as similar to standing before the Glorified Christ at the Last Judgment.

that familiar Catholic liturgy by extending the consecration of bread and wine to the consecration of the Cosmos.

> Once upon a time men took into your temple the first fruits of their harvests, the flower of their flocks. But the offering you really want, the offering [of a return of love from your creation] you mysteriously need every day to appease your hunger, to slake your thirst is nothing less than the growth of the world borne ever onwards in the stream of universal becoming. Receive, O Lord, this all-embracing host which your whole creation, moved by your magnetism, offers you at this dawn of a new day.[140]

Teilhard, like every person participating in the liturgy, was confronted with a decision. Humans, because we are self-reflective, have the trait for religious thinking, and possess free will, are free to respond or not to our expanding consciousness of God at work in the Cosmos. Of his personal communion with God in the cosmic liturgy, Teilhard writes,

> Lord, lock me up in the deepest depths of your heart; and then, holding me there, burn me, purify me, set me on fire, sublimate me, till I become utterly what you would have me be, through the utter annihilation of my ego [my false self].[141]

Teilhard's grammar was influenced by Catholic devotions which describe the Heart of Christ being on fire with love of the world. These devotional prayers ask that our hearts may become like his, a complete oblation of love for God which purifies and refines the

---

140. Teilhard de Chardin, Hymn of the Universe (NY: Harper & Row, 1961), https://d2y1pz2y630308.cloudfront.net/5520/documents/2016/10/The%20Mass%20On%20The%20World.pdf
141. Ibid., 7.

truth of the created goodness within us. This truth is our relationship as partners-in-being with God and all the Cosmos. This is the truth residing at the heart of matter. It is the truth that Christ reveals in his own person by his sacrifice on the cross, self-emptying love which is the remedy for sin and the completion of our likeness to God.

In this way Teilhard calls upon the power of transmutation that Swimme recognizes in the universe and in each of us. Transmutation is the power that effects change in a person. Transmutation is a power not self-generated but received just by our participation in the Cosmos. Just by the fact that our life's journey is one of ongoing relationships with God and with others, we cannot be in this universe without undergoing constant change. This power is at our disposal in the struggle to be one's truest self, the self which is known to the creator and mirrored in the Cosmic Christ.

Sharing communion with God in Christ during the celebration of the Eucharist manifests another power of the universe, the power of transformation, the power by which the whole is changed because of the change in each individual. This power at work in the actions of the worshipping community, who become agents of the transformation of Earth and its creatures, creates a synergistic communion transforming the whole. These powers are signs of the ongoing creative power of God sustaining the world and drawing it to fulfillment. For Teilhard, these powers coursing through the universe and, therefore, all of us are summed up in Christ's total offering of himself for the life of the world.

Teilhard had begun writing portions of his Mass as early as 1917 and completed it in 1923 in the Ordos Desert during his first archaeological trip to China. Oblate priest and theologian Ron Rolheiser gives some insight into how Teilhard's writing was greeted during his lifetime.

> Pierre Teilhard de Chardin was once called to Rome and asked to clarify certain issues in regard to his teachings. At one point, he was asked: 'What are you trying to do?' His answer, in effect: 'I am trying to write a Christology that is wide enough to incorporate Christ. Christ isn't just an anthropological phenomenon with significance for humanity, but Christ is also a cosmic event with significance for the planet.'[142]

Nevertheless, after his writings were posthumously published, the Vatican's doctrinal office warned that they were filled with ambiguities and doctrinal errors.

Decades later, in 2009, Teilhard's vision of the cosmic liturgy and his place in it as a priest received public recognition from Pope Benedict XVI, much to the consternation of traditionalist Catholics. In a homily on the life and liturgical ministry of Catholic priests, Benedict used the word "host" according to its technical Latin meaning. A host is the "sacrifice" offered in a liturgy. He said,

> The role of the priesthood is to consecrate the world so that it may become a living host...so that the liturgy may not be something alongside the reality of the world, but that the world itself shall become a living host, a liturgy. This is also the great vision of Teilhard de Chardin: in the end we shall achieve a true

---

142. Ron Rolheiser, O.M.I., "The Cosmic Christ," November 25, 2001. https://ronrolheiser.com/the-cosmic-christ/, accessed July 10, 2020.

cosmic liturgy, where the cosmos becomes a living host. And let us pray the Lord to help us become priests in this sense, to aid in the transformation of the world, in adoration of God, beginning with ourselves. [143]

Pope Benedict, shaped by his personal engagement in the dialogue between science and theology, affirmed Teilhard's vision of a cosmic liturgy as a vision larger than many priests may have recognized. Rolheiser made a similar point about Teilhard,

> What's implied here, among other things, is that Christ is bigger than the historical churches, operates beyond the scope of historical Christianity (although admittedly he does operate within it), and has influences prior and beyond human history itself. It is Christ, visible and invisible – the person, the spirit, the power, and the mystery – who is drawing all things, physical and spiritual, natural and religious, non-Christian and Christian, into one. As Kenneth Cragg put it: 'It will take all the religions of the world to give full expression to the whole Christ.'[144]

Language about Christ, Christology

Christology literally means talking about Christ. The context for this talk is the faith of a community of his followers. As such, Christology is the ongoing clarification of the faith community's understanding of Christ. The grammar of Christology, the basic elements of language used to communicate the community's

---

143. Homily of His Holiness Benedict XVI, Vespers, Cathedral of Aosta, Italy, 24 July 2009, Libreria Editrice Vaticana. https://www.vatican.va/content/ benedict-xvi/en/homilies/2009/documents/hf_ben-xvi_hom_20090724_vespri-aosta.html
144. Albert Kenneth Cragg, (1913-2012), was an Anglican Bishop and Missiologist. Quoted by Ronald Rolheiser, https://ronrolheiser.com/the-cosmic-christ/

experience of Christ, necessarily develops over time as the possibilities inherent in his person continue to coalesce into greater clarity. We can see this development was already occurring in the last four decades of the first century as the Christian scriptures were being written. That development has continued over two millennia as communities strive to understand Christ within their own cultural worldviews. In his Mass on the World, Teilhard was offering some new grammar for Christology, language that reflected twentieth century cosmology.

This book is an initial attempt to present Christology in dialogue with the new story of the Cosmos. At the same time, the effort here is to remain faithful to the doctrinal teaching about Christ that has been handed down over two millennia, as we contextualize it in the new story of the evolution of the Cosmos. That is what Teilhard was attempting, to remain within the context of Roman Catholic Christology as he expressed his vision of the Cosmic Christ. Through his Mass on the World, Teilhard wanted to give expression to his understanding of Christ in light of the new scientific evidence of the evolution of the Cosmos. He believed the story of Jesus that had been told among Christians for millennia was not only compatible with the new story of the evolution of the Cosmos but was able to uniquely complete that story. Christology since Teilhard reflects Cragg's comment that all the world's religions are needed to fully explain Christ. Theologians are currently trying to enculturate traditional teachings concerning Jesus the Christ into the cultural worldviews of various peoples. Christology was primarily understood for centuries, especially in the west, as cognitive assertions which were to clarify the faith of Christians. These assertions were logical intellectual statements about Christ. However, theologians since the Second Vatican Council (1962-1965) have striven to return to the methodology of the earliest Christian writers. These early writers were by and large pastors whose theologies developed within the faith experience of their churches whose cultural worldviews varied significantly. They contextualized Christ's gospel in the circumstances and cultures of the peoples they addressed. It is important for our discussion here to understand that this return to the methodology of these ancient writers provides a means of responding to the changes in our worldview advanced by modern science and shaping our current cultural circumstances.

Teilhard expressed his vision of Christ as the Omega Point where all the elements of the Cosmos would finally converge. He was using the grammar of science and theology available in his day. Teilhard's thought was profoundly influenced by the popular 1907 book *Creative Evolution,* which concentrated on the "Élan vital" or life force at work in living organisms and within the Cosmos.[145] It was reminiscent of the Greek philosopher Aristotle (383-322 B.C.E.) who taught that the whole is greater than, exceeds its parts. A living organism is so much more than the physical parts of which it is composed and of

---

145. Henri Bergson, trans. Arthur Mitchell, <u>Creative Evolution</u> (Mineola, NY: Dover Publishing, 1907).

the causes and effects these parts bring about. Life appears to be something more than material existence alone can account for.

The Gifford Lectures at Glasgow in 1916–18 and 1921–22, by Samuel Alexander and C. Lloyd Morgan respectively, dealt with a fuller definition of evolution beyond natural selection. These lectures concentrated interest among scientists on the dynamics of emergence and synergy as aspects of evolution. They sought to account for the evolutionary emergence of mind, culture, and religion. They even suggested a telos, or completion, toward which the world was moving. Teilhard used this grammar of the philosophy of science to express his vision of an emerging Noosphere, or growing evolutionary consciousness, and an Omega Point for the Cosmos, a fulfillment in Christ.[146] Before Teilhard's death in 1955, science had advanced rapidly in its understanding of the Cosmos, and many of his contemporary critics point out his writings did not incorporate those advances. Of course, the criticism is factually correct. However, Teilhard had been required by his superiors under the vow of obedience not to write or publish further on these topics.

Professional theological research and writing during the same period expanded the grammar of Christology. Nevertheless, the

---

146. The Noosphere is an analogy, like the atmosphere which envelops Earth and fosters life. It is the collective human mind forming an envelope of conscious awareness through which the material world may be given a new form of life. The Omega Point is the completion of the Cosmos toward which the powers of the universe are spiraling. However, it is not simply a perfection brought about by natural created powers alone but a Cosmic fulfillment through union with and in the person of Christ, the Incarnate Word of God.

leadership of the Catholic Church did not relinquish its static hold on public theology until the Second Vatican Council in the latter half of the twentieth century. It was only after the council that the expanded grammar of Christology became commonly available. There was, however, a cosmic vision of Jesus the Christ that had been continuously operative for two millennia. The cosmic nature of Christ was present in the Christian scriptures and in the Liturgy of the Eucharist. Teilhard's Catholic faith was formed by both. His studies in anthropology provided him with a new understanding of Cosmic emergence as a context for his faith in the cosmic fulfillment promised in Jesus the Christ.

Conclusion

The good news Teilhard believed is that in the person of Jesus the Christ God is bringing humankind, and through us the whole of creation, to its fulfillment. We will examine this good news more thoroughly in the following chapters. For now, we look more deeply into the encounters others had with Jesus during his earthly ministry and what they came to believe about him. By doing so we hope to expand our understanding of Jesus, to deepen our appreciation of the truth his humanity was expressing. This is what Christology is all about, an ongoing discovery of the truth revealed in our ongoing encounters with Jesus the Christ.

Chapter X

Christology as Encounter

The Humanity of Christ

For many centuries, the divinity of Jesus was emphasized in Christology. That emphasis was based on the Aristotelian principle that the whole of an organism exceeds the parts. While Christology declared that Jesus was fully both human and divine, he was considered a divine person, because his humanity had been taken up by the Word of God. Jesus, then, is God in human existence. This perspective led in the popular mind to a certain distancing of Jesus from human experience. How could a divine person suffer on the one hand and not know everything on the other? This was the case even though the humanity of the historical person, Jesus of Nazareth, is clearly acknowledged in the New Testament and, consequently, in subsequent Christological teaching.

In his writing about human encounter, John Henry Newman (1801–1890) described what he called the "illative sense" by which we come to know things more truly.[147] Our knowledge of other persons is not limited to simple physical or even historical information about them. Using our illative sense we can add depth and breadth to our knowledge through encounter, gradually accumulating new possibilities for understanding. These coalesce over time as a greater certainty about the person, a deeper awareness. Of course, Newman's illative sense is an appeal to the human trait of empathy, which provides us a certain truth through personal encounter. This is the way he believed doctrinal assertions about Christ developed over time, because of the possibility of ongoing encounter with Christ.

---

147. More explanation of Newman's "illative sense" is available in chapter XII.

Newman was an English theologian, scholar, and Anglican priest who in 1845 came to full communion with the Roman Catholic Church. In 1879, he was made a Cardinal of the Roman Church by Pope Leo XIII. He believed Christian doctrines constitute a record of the possibilities concerning the person of Jesus which have led over time to increasing certainty about his person, as well as his personal presence with and ongoing work among us.

The Christian scriptures were written after the death and resurrection of Jesus. They were written within divergent cultural communities of Christians. We can see a pattern of development in the Christian scriptures which. reveals a growing certainty about the person of Jesus among these various churches. The certainty included conviction of his presence among them as risen Lord and his pre-existence as the Son or Word of God. Through ongoing encounter with the man known as Jesus of Nazareth, during his ministry and after his resurrection, the churches became more aware of his being God incarnate. Such development of its teachings has continued down to our present day through the Church's ongoing encounter of Christ. Teilhard was continuing the development of doctrinal understanding by extending the encounter of Christ with the entire Cosmos. To do so, he used the new science of cosmic evolution as the context in which further possibilities of encounter might be discerned. But using the material sciences as a context for encountering Christ was not the norm for Christology until decades later.

As Newman's illative sense influenced doctrinal development in the twentieth century, we came to define a human person as an experiencing self who is involved with truth. That means each person is recognized as an agent of truth; a person's life manifests a truth about herself. Each person becomes more truly herself depending on how she acts in her relations with the whole to which she belongs. It is in this way she can *love-in-truth*.

When this understanding of the human person, an experiencing self who is involved with truth, is applied to Jesus the Christ, Christians say he is Truth itself. By his outpouring of love for God and us, Jesus expressed in his humanity, especially his ministry and death on the cross, the truth about God's love for the world. Responding to Pilot's questioning about his purpose in the world, Jesus said, "I have come to testify to the truth."[148] His person is the truth about our humanity which is to find our fulfillment in God, as he did. And the truth about God who is drawing us through Christ to share the divine life. In a similar way, Christ reveals the truth about the Cosmos beyond what science can apprehend because science cannot apprehend that the Cosmos has any purpose, but in Christ, whose humanity is part of the Cosmos, its purpose is to have its fulfillment in divine transcendence.

This development of doctrine has given place to enculturation of the faith among the various societies around the world. A leader in this development, French theologian Henri de Lubac, S.J. (1896-1991), emphasized in his theology of church that post-modern societies needed to be in touch with the humanity of Jesus, if they were to accept that through his humanity, we come to share his divinity. His insight had a profound effect on theologians in the second half of the twentieth century. They emphasized that the humanity of Jesus reveals a profound truth about humanity itself.

In his humanity, Jesus is the point of contact between humankind and God, and so between Cosmology and Christology. He reveals in himself the truth about humanity, the universe of which we are a part, and thus about the creator. As such, Jesus is the heart of matter and the head of the Cosmos, fully revealing the plan of God in creating the world to bring it to completion as sons and daughters of God. As St. Ambrose (C.E. 339-397) wrote,

---

148. John 18:37.

This adoption of sons is that of the whole body of creation, when it will be as it were a son of God and see the divine, eternal goodness face to face.[149]

Encountering Jesus of Nazareth

The four written Gospels are not videos, so we cannot see for ourselves the humanity of Jesus and how those who encountered him experienced the truth about themselves, creation, and God. Instead, the Gospels are witnesses' accounts of events in the life of this man and of how these events affected him and those who witnessed them. As witness accounts, the Gospels allow the reader to have an encounter with the person of Jesus through the shared encounters of his first disciples.

For many readers, the idea of encounter is limited to experiencing some physical presence. However, language, both oral and written, makes human encounters unique. In 1979, Franz Jozef van Beeck, S.J. published *Christ Proclaimed: Christology as Rhetoric* in which he explained that language is more than logical assertions about persons or things[150] As humanistic psychology points out, language, which includes a variety of signs and symbolic means of expression, is an exercise in encounter between persons. The four Gospels are such language encounters with Jesus, and in those encounters, we can see that his way of being related to others is as a partner-in-being.

To be partners-in-being is defined as follows. Every person has the capacity to exist in a particular way, to exist freely and originally as her own self with other persons, not as competitors but as partners-in-being and letting-be. Being-related is to be with another as the whole person you are. Refusal of being-related is to create a false self. Why? Because by refusing encounter, I am claiming that I

---

149. Ambrose of Milan, Letter 35, quoted in Liturgy of the Hours, III, p.184 (NY: Catholic Book Publishing Corp., 1975).
150. Franz Jozef van Beeck, S.J., Christ Proclaimed: Christology as Rhetoric (NY: Paulist Press, 1979).

have no ability, or cannot recognize the ability in you, to be anything other than a competitor rather than a partner-in-being. That claim is a lie, falsifying myself and/or attempting to falsify you. It is reminiscent of Adam and Eve's hiding themselves from God after eating from the forbidden tree and then blaming the snake, each other, and by implication, God. They hid themselves because in their willfulness, they were competitors with God and with other creatures, rather than the partners-in-being they were created to become. We, their descendants, do the same.

On the other hand, in any encounter, as partners-in-being I can represent you and you me. By representing each other we have empathy for each other. This happens as we appreciate each other's experiences of life, walk in each other's shoes. This is one of the benefits of language, it enables encounter, the sharing of selves. Language as encounter even allows suffering to be enriching. When compassion is the foundation of your life with others, your actions will be characterized by care and responsible stewardship. If your compassion includes undergoing suffering, that same compassion can be extended, even to the person who is inflicting the suffering.

The Gospels were written by persons who encountered Jesus, found in him a partner-in-being who had compassion for others, and saw that he accepted suffering with compassion, even for those who inflicted it. In these encounters, Jesus revealed the truth about what it means to be related-in-being with the whole to which we belong. Encounters with Christ were necessary for his disciples to understand him as a partner-in-being, and through their encounters with his humanity to understand how he was so much more. What they discovered about him was given voice in the titles they gave him after his death and resurrection.

The multiple titles of Jesus in the Gospels, like Christ, Son of Man, and Son of God, are part of the grammar of Christology among his first disciples. These titles present him both as very human and as sharing divinity with God. His given name was *Y'suah* in Hebrew or

Joshua in English. The name means "The Lord is salvation." Jesus is the Latin spelling of his name. Christ is not his family name but from the Greek translation of Messiah, a Hebrew title meaning "Anointed." Calling him "Jesus the Christ" indicates this man from Nazareth in Galilee is "The one anointed to be for us God's salvation." That is the good news, or "Godspell" in old English, that Christians believe.

For his first disciples to encounter Jesus was to encounter the one who was fully human. That is why Roger Haight suggests in *Jesus, Symbol of God* that we begin our understanding of Jesus with his ministry where the truth about his humanity is most easily perceived.[151] In the New Testament, Jesus was known as the son of a carpenter in Nazareth, a town in northern Israel, and a carpenter himself. He had a mother named Mary and other relatives from the same area, Galilee, where he lived most of his life. Galilee was a territory of mixed ethnicity. It was an agricultural area which included an inland freshwater sea, while its larger cities along that sea to the east and the Mediterranean coast to the west were international hubs. There are a few references to the historicity of Jesus written by Roman historians and magistrates within a century of his death in 33 C.E. The oldest by Josephus (37-100) mentions his crucifixion. However, most of our knowledge of him is found in the writings of his followers written between 50-100 C.E., the period when his first disciples were dying. Their preaching and writing needed to be

---

151. Roger Haight, S.J., Jesus, Symbol of God (Maryknoll, NY: Orbis Books, 1999). Haight was disciplined by the Vatican for how he has shaped his Christology in dialogue with the post-modern culture. The concern was that he was not preserving the authentic belief of the Church about Christ's dual natures in his attempt to make it understandable in contemporary western culture. However, his encouragement to begin with the ministry of Jesus for a better understanding of Christ is in line with other contemporary theologians whose work is approved.
https://www.catholicculture.org/culture/library/view.cfm?recnum=8736

recorded and shared more broadly with the growing numbers of Christians.

The effects his ministry had on others flowed from his being-related to them as partners-in-being. For instance, John Pilch (1935-2016), who taught the cultural world of the bible for eighteen years at Georgetown University, says Jesus offered a very different way of dealing with hierarchical status in a culture absolutely controlled by it.[152] Having discovered that his closest disciples were arguing who among them was the greatest, Jesus placed a child in their midst, and putting his arms around the child, he said to them, "Whoever receives one child such as this in my name, receives me; and whoever receives me, receives not me but the one who sent me."[153] But a child had no standing in the honor-bound social conditions in which his disciples lived. Jesus was turning social relationships as his disciples knew them upside down. For him, power was manifest not by competition but by empathy. That was the way he knew God to be, and why he could also say whoever received him received not just him but the God who sent him.

The relationship of Jesus with God, the Father who missioned him to fulfill creation, was not a relationship of competition. Their relationship was of such empathy Jesus could teach that he and the Father were One.[154] In the Roman social system fathers had complete life and death control over all the members of their households. Jesus taught there is only one Father, who is in heaven, and whoever did that Father's will was brother and sister and mother to Jesus.[155] Clearly, he recognized both himself as a son of God, with whom he had his primary relationship, and others who sought God as his true family.

---

152. John J. Pilch, <u>The Cultural World of Jesus, Sunday by Sunday, Cycle B</u> (Collegeville, MN: Liturgical Press, 1996).
153. Mark 9:37.
154. John 10:30.
155. Matthew 23:9, John 18:37, and Mark 3:33-34.

He also destabilized the absolute authority both of government and of religion, and in doing so he claimed a unique status for himself. Jesus told Pilot during his capital trial that the governor would have no authority over him unless it were given by God. Then, by not answering Pilot's further interrogation, Jesus was not just risking death, he was specifically defining his death in relation to God's authority, the highest authority in his life, like a son to his father.[156]

To the High Priest, while on trial for blasphemy, Jesus applied to himself the biblical title Son of Man, a prophetic title referencing the power of God being given to a human being, to someone like us.[157] Clearly, Jesus had a sense of being-related to God and to other humans that was both profoundly Jewish and yet in a fuller way than his priest-judges had ever experienced. That is why the High Priest sought to put Jesus to death, because by claiming this title Jesus claimed to be equal with God. That was blasphemous to his judges. Still, it appears in the gospels that this title, Son of Man, was his preferred self-identifying title throughout his ministry. This title allows for his equality with God in his mission of being partner-in-being with creation, and at the same time it allowed his being a servant of God like the prophets before him.[158]

The Miracles of Christ

The Christian scriptures present Jesus during his earthly ministry as exercising the divine power to freely interact with all of nature. In his sermon on the Jewish feast of Pentecost, Peter addresses the Jews and others assembled in Jerusalem and says, "Jesus the Nazorean was *a man* commended to you by God with mighty deeds, wonders, and signs, which God worked through him in your midst, as you

---

156. John 19:10-11.
157. Mark 14:61-62, Daniel 7:13–14.
158. Ezekiel 2:3-6.

yourselves know."[159] From the perspective of modern science, what are we to make of these miracles of Jesus, the man from Nazareth?

The free interaction of God with creation has bedeviled science for generations since the time of Isaac Newton (1642–1727) who was born a year after the death of Galileo. Newton was instrumental in spreading the scientific method for the observation and testing of facts among English speaking peoples, as their empire was beginning global expansion. David Hume (1711–1776), a Scottish philosopher, applied the scientific method to the study of human nature, especially the mind and human behavior. Hume's intention was to remove any religious thinking and rely solely on the testing of observable facts. Hume, for instance, insisted that miracles could not be tested and, therefore, any report of a miracle was dependent on faulty human testimony alone. Newton and Hume are considered principal representatives of the enlightenment science brought to humankind.

Samuel Taylor Coleridge (1772-1817), the great English poet of Romanticism, led a reaction to Hume's theories. Coleridge noted that the human mind was given the gift of self-consciousness without which observation and testing could not occur. Yet, self-consciousness, an inward power of mind, was not in itself observable. One could only observe the way self-consciousness enables humans to interact with the whole to which they belong. Coleridge's observation of the inwardness of human consciousness led to his insight that there is an inwardness to the whole of material reality. Beauty, goodness, and truth are not simply observable facts but the inward transcendent form of the Cosmos. He believed the rules that governed nature included these transcendent forms. He reasoned that those rules were not being suspended when a miracle occurred.

---

159. Acts 2:22, emphasis added. Here and in many other New Testament texts (e.g., I John 1:42, 2 John 1:7, Matthew 1:21, Luke 1:35 and 24:39) there is an emphasis on the humanity of Christ, because one of the earliest contradictions of Christian faith was Docetism, from the Greek word for "to appear," which stressed that Jesus only appeared to have a human body and, therefore, a human nature.

Instead, the very inner form of nature was responding to and manifesting itself in response to the Goodness of God. This is what we observe as miraculous.

Certainly, Coleridge seems to have grasped the meaning of miracle that the Gospels intended. In the case of the miracles of Jesus, nature was responding to the presence in him of the eternal beauty, goodness and truth of which nature was the image. Nature was responding to the presence of God. The Christian scriptures proclaim that the fullness of these transcendent qualities dwelt in Jesus as Son of God. In his miracles, nature was responding to the presence of that fullness which is God. It appears in each of his miracles that the powers which course through the universe were responding to the fullness of the divine presence in Jesus.

His miracles seem to be the observable manifestation of the very title Son of Man, which references the power of God being given to a human being, to someone like us. Like humans who encountered him and experienced an encounter with God, other things in nature responded to his presence as if to the creative power of God sustaining and drawing them to fulfillment. These responses were various and awe inspiring. For instance storms on the sea became calm, a bit of bread and fish multiplied to feed thousands, persons possessed by forces beyond the control of humans were freed. But these miracles raised questions among his contemporaries about the source of his power, and that had consequences for Jesus himself.

As witnessed accounts, the Gospels tell how some of his detractors claimed it was by the power of demons that he worked his miracles, not by the power of God. They recall how he was rejected by religious authorities because he forgave sins, a power that belonged only to God. The Gospels also say he touched a leper and healed him, only to be unable, like a leper himself, to enter a village because his reputation made the crowds impossible to negotiate. He ate with the morally unclean and even with tax collectors, collaborators in the Roman occupation, thus taking their uncleanness

173

on himself. Whether a father whose daughter was dying or a woman whose hemorrhage doctors could not heal, Jesus in his encounters affirmed their faith in him. Their faith, he indicated, mediated their healing.

His encounters were not limited to Jews. A Roman centurion who wanted his servant healed placed his faith in Jesus, who then expressed amazement at the man humble faith. Jesus said he had been sent for this very purpose, as healing for the sick and forgiveness for sinners. His miracles demonstrated his empathy with the suffering. More profoundly, in each encounter Jesus himself made it clear the healing and forgiveness he offered was an encounter with God.

The Sufferings of Christ

These encounters with the humanity of Jesus allow us to relate to him as one like us, even as they suggest his uniqueness among us. In his encounters creation was encountering the power of the God of the Jews, whom Jesus freely proclaimed had sent him. This sending is not like a superman coming from another planet or an angel coming from another spiritual realm. Instead, to be sent is to be missioned. God had given Jesus a mission to accomplish. In the Gospel according to Luke, the ministry of Jesus is described by a quote from the prophet Isaiah,

> The spirit of the Lord God is upon me, because the Lord has anointed me; he has sent me to bring glad tidings to the lowly, to heal the brokenhearted, to proclaim liberty to the captives and release to the prisoners, to announce a year of favor from the Lord.[160]

In his encounters with the suffering, Jesus both represented God, showing God's compassion for the suffering, and he represented

---

160. Luke 4:14-21, quoting Isaiah 61:1-2.

those who were suffering, who in their suffering hoped for God's compassion. He did the same in his death on a cross, assuring a man crucified next to him that they would be together in paradise that same day. In his ministry, even to the hour of his death, an encounter with Jesus was an experience of partnership-in-being with God.

The casual reader may think these descriptions of Jesus in the Gospels are simply the way his disciples showed reverence for their great teacher. But there is more to the man that both discomforted them and motivated their deeper encounter with God. Edith Hamilton (1867-1963), an expert on ancient cultures, left us her thoughts on the discomforting Jesus in *Witness to the Truth: Christ and his Interpreters.*[161] She points out that the gospel accounts of the discomforting words and deeds of Jesus are a witness to his real manner of teaching and behaving. Why else would his disciples, who lived in the honor-bound society of his day, risk sharing these things that call into question his honor and theirs as his followers?

His death on the cross was the complete dehumanization of a person which Roman law inflicted upon non-citizens. And yet his crucifixion was in every way a fulfillment of his life and teaching, laying down his life because, as he announced, that was what God had sent him to do. God had sent him to fully represent human suffering and death by his own. Jesus is presented as the New Adam, the universal particular representing the vulnerability to death and suffering of every sentient creature since life began to evolve. As the universal particular, his resurrection promised a like transcendence of all the death and suffering in the history of the Cosmos into an abundance of life.

When Peter tried to dissuade him from suffering crucifixion, Jesus responded by telling Peter he was thinking not as God does but as human beings do.[162] Peter was demonstrating a pragmatic vision of

---

161. Edith Hamilton, Witness to the Truth: Christ and his interpreters (NY: W.W. Norton, 1962), 149-152.
162. Mark 8:31-33.

what a Messiah and Son of God should be in the hierarchical culture in which he lived. Instead, Jesus insisted doing the Father's will was the food that nourished him.

In our times, many are scandalized by the idea that God would send his son to die for the salvation of the world. That is understandable based on a desire to be more inclusive of the dignity of each person and reject any victimization as abhorrent. However, the death of Jesus on a cross was to heal our cunning human willfulness, which uses one's own welfare as the measure of what is good. Therefore, Paul called Jesus a Second Adam, because by his death he frees the human will to find its true fulfillment in the goodness of God.

Jesus was a new Adam, the foundation of a new humanity, by his willingness to bring the whole of which he was a part to its fulfillment in God. To do so meant enduring what all humans endure, death. Jesus, however, freely accepted the experience of death as an expression of the self-emptying love by which God created the world.[163] Laying down his life, so that he could take it up again in a fuller way, revealed his Father's will for humankind, not death but fullness of life. In that way, he also could fully express how he is the Son of God, by finding his immortality in loving God more than life itself. The fullness of life he revealed in his resurrection was to be the fruit of the tree of the cross, the new Tree of Life in the true garden of God, the Kingdom of Heaven.[164] This fruit is what Christians celebrate in the Liturgy of the Eucharist, what the boy's Italian grandmother asked him to recognize in a piece of bread fallen on the floor, and what Teilhard celebrated in his Mass on the World as he consecrated the whole Cosmos as an offering of thanksgiving to the creator.

---

163. I Corinthians 15:16-28.
164. John 4:34.

Conclusion

In Teilhard's vision of the Cosmos, Christ is the foundation of a new way of being related. Just as there is a biological way in which all things are interrelated, there is also a unique way in which human consciousness is interrelated. That unique means of interrelatedness is love or compassion uniting all creation. Teilhard did not reduce Christ to a solely Christian experience. Instead, he sought to universalize the effect of the person of Jesus upon the whole world and gather its collective consciousness through Christ to its completion in God. In the next chapter, we will consider further this uniqueness of the person of Jesus the Christ within the Cosmos.

Chapter XI

Evolving Consciousness

Our Scientific Understanding

From the outset of this book, we have looked at the differing perspectives of science and religious traditions. Cosmology, as a branch of astrophysics, is the study of the universe's origin, its large-scale structures and dynamics, and the fate of the universe, including the laws of science that govern these areas. We learn from the perspective of astrophysics about the evolution of the universe since the Big Bang. But the new cosmology is a branch of philosophy which tries to explain the presence of life-forms on Earth, especially of human observers of the Cosmos. The philosophy of cosmology tells us life has always been a possibility in the universe since the Big Bang. But, as human observers of the Cosmos, the only life we know is that on Earth.

Through the work of evolutionary biology and anthropology, we know life on Earth began around 4.2 billion years ago. While we do not know yet if there is life anywhere else in the universe, we suspect we are not the only life-forms. Our species, Homo sapiens, evolved around 300,000 years ago from previous species. Since then, there has not been sufficient time for the evolution of a new species of humans. However, it is anticipated that we will continue to evolve over the next billion years, unless all human life meets its end in a natural cataclysm or one that is intentionally willed.

Our evolved ability for self-consciousness has its roots in our ability to perceive the world through our senses. We reflect first upon sensorial experiences. Through sensory awareness we gradually perceive our interdependence with other creatures, with each other in the human community, with Earth itself. We are not a finished product any more than the universe itself. Indeed, we are constituted by our relationships, which is why we are relational beings and not just individuals who may or may not choose to relate to each other. As such, we recognize that all life-forms exceed, are greater than, the matter alone of which they are made.

We humans have an intellect by which we reflect upon our sensory experiences to produce reflective observations of the world around us and within us. We also test our sensory experiences and our observations for consistency. Thus we come to know how both we and the world function. With the evolved trait for religious thinking and through our encounters with each other and the rest of creation, we are gradually led beyond what we can perceive with our senses. Creation itself has led humans to experience life as an encounter with the numinous, with beauty, goodness, and truth. Utilizing the trait for religious thinking, humans developed wisdom traditions and the societies these traditions sustain. These many and varied traditions interpreted our experience of the numinous on Earth and in the Cosmos as a whole. Among these traditions, the name often given to the fullness of the numinous is "the creator."

Judeo-Christian Understanding

From the perspective of Jewish faith, the creator-God shared the divine goodness with every creature, each manifesting that goodness in its own unique way. The work of creation was given into the care of humankind. This implies that there was more to creation than a finished product. The creator partnered with humankind to sustain creation and make it fruitful. Thus, the Jewish scriptures contain stories of our being accompanied by God who sustains creation as it evolves toward its fulfillment. In those stories, God allures humans so that we can find our fulfillment in divine transcendence manifest on Earth as love of God, each other, and all creation.

These stories include the call of Abraham to faith in One God, the commandments given through Moses that fashioned a people who mirrored God's faithfulness to creation and to life on Earth, and they included the ritual worship of God as the greatest good, as well as moral teachings about human freedom and dignity. These stories teach us that we are not simply evolved mammals seeking our own self-preservation. We are called by the creator-God into an encounter that creates a future. That future is fullness of life for the whole world.

According to the Book of Genesis, our first human parents, in an effort to sustain life in the face of death and the many other vulnerabilities within creation, taught us, their descendants, to use our perception of our own welfare as the measure of good and evil in creation. James Allison in *The Joy of Being Wrong* offers great insight into how this teaching continues to be passed from one generation to the next.[165] Like other mammals, we learn to value what our parents and peers value. Bears teach their cubs what to eat and where to find it. Humans, by their behaviors, identify for their children what to seek in life. Thus, we begin to want the things that seem to be pleasing to the eye and good to have, whether it is the toy another child chooses, our parents' politics, or the attention our classmate receives.

This formation takes place before we attain the rational ability to make choices for the good of the larger whole to which we belong. But as John Gibbs reminds us, morality involves truths about our obligations that are inherent in the maintenance and development of human interconnectedness with each other and all life-forms.[166] As we mature, one of our essential tasks is to recognize that we are continuing to desire the goods someone else desired, a desire we thought was original to ourselves. If we do not achieve this insight, we will continue to use what we falsely understand to be our own

---

165. James Allison, The Joy of Being Wrong: Original sin through Easter eyes (NY: Crossroads Publishing, 1998).
166. John C. Gibbs, Moral Development and Reality: Beyond the theories of Kohlberg, Hoffman, and Haidt, Fourth Edition (NY: Oxford University Press, 2019).

passionate vision of life, instead of the passionate vision offered uniquely to us through the numinous. For the Christian, that vision is a truth hidden in the goodness of the world, in our interconnectedness with all life and its creator, specifically focused through Christ. One can appreciate why parents are reminded at the baptism of a child that they are taking on the responsibility of rearing their child in the practice of the faith that the sacrament empowers in their child, a numinous vision focused through the death and resurrection of Christ.

Religious thinking allows us to experience the allure of the numinous, but its allure is toward something that we cannot simply possess. Instead, the numinous is beyond our grasp even as it effects transcendence in us. Because this truth feels uncomfortable, an individual may decide never to trust or use the impetus of religious thinking. Moral thinking seeks what is good so that we may use it well. But without the transcendence offered by the numinous, our human will is insufficient to motivate care of the whole to which we belong. It is the numinous, understood through our religious thinking, which clarifies our vision of the whole and motivates us to foster its care through self-emptying love. We cannot simply possess the numinous for our own use, but instead are transformed by it.

The Genesis myth of the fall illustrates the insufficiency of our human will. We use it to preserve our own welfare, which becomes the sole measure of what is good. The result is missing the mark, the path the creator set out for our fulfillment. The full measure of our humanity is not our personal welfare as we define it but our likeness to God to which we are called and empowered.

For the Hebrew, being made in God's image was the path to acting as God acts, so to enter into God's likeness. For this reason, commandments were given through Moses. The commandments were directions on the path to divine likeness, which could only be achieved by fostering life with others in our human community, with other life-forms, and with Earth itself. The history of humankind was our struggle to follow this path to divine likeness. That struggle is part of the history of the Cosmos. If one part were to find its fulfillment in God, the Hebrew faith trusted the whole of which we are a part also will do so. God, through the numinous, mentors us along this path and allures us to its fulfillment.

From the Christian perspective, the way to the fulfillment of humankind and of the universe is the person of Jesus the Christ who fulfilled the commandments for us. In him, our humanity is more than a moral struggle to seek the welfare of the whole to which we belong. Our greater human struggle is to move beyond the good we can achieve (transcend the good within creation) and accept the gift of life in abundance, a gift that through Christ is already emerging within the Cosmos. This gift is likeness to God who is self-emptying love. Self-emptying love is the power of cataclysm in human life that makes possible the emergence of the fullness of life, a relational way of being in which all share God's way of being, love. This way was revealed in the death and resurrection of Jesus. Following in the way of self-emptying love is an old perspective enshrined in the commandment to love God with our whole self. It has become a completely new perspective on the fullness of our humanity as revealed in the risen Christ for the fulfillment of the Cosmos. Now we have hope of a new heaven and a new Earth emerging in God's very likeness.

Teilhard de Chardin believed humanity's consciousness, using the trait for religious thinking, was growing toward this Christian hope. He sought to present this uniquely hopeful vision for the Cosmos to a world torn by war and human conflict. This Christian perspective was first made evident in the scriptures and the celebration of the Liturgy of the Eucharist, and now he believed it is perceivable in the evolution of the universe. Teilhard called this ever-emerging collective human consciousness the Noosphere. He came to this religious perspective on Christ in dialogue with the perspective of evolutionary science. Science was the context for his contemplation of Christ as the Omega Point of the Cosmos.

The unique place of Jesus the Christ in the evolution of the Cosmos is to bring about its fulfillment through self-emptying love. The Christian perspective on Christ as self-emptying love (*kenosis* in Greek) was first enshrined in the ancient hymn Paul recorded in his letter to the Philippians. There we see the pattern of self-emptying in Christ which Paul suggests must be the pattern among Christians.[167] All that God had created by divine *ekstasis* will return through *kenosis* to fulfillment in its source. For Teilhard, Jesus the Christ is the Omega Point, the point where all the self-emptying love within the universe is gathered to its fulfillment in God.

Christ's Self-awareness

The Christian scriptures show that his first Jewish disciples encountered, in the person of Jesus of Nazareth, a new humanity filled with the fullness of God. While among his own disciples, Jesus encountered ways of thinking and behaving that were self-serving and competitive. He repeatedly offered his disciples teaching and example on how to shed that false self. When they wondered how often one must forgive, Jesus had some sobering words to offer. Peter asked if seven times fulfilled the teaching. Jesus answered, "No. I say seventy times seven."[168]

He taught that violence is not solved by more violence; the only solution is forgiveness, which is limitless, seventy times seven times. Thus, he overturned the Genesis account of Lamech, who in response to any injury swore to multiply that act of violence seventy-seven times in settling the score.[169] This Lamech was the father of Noah to whom God said Earth must be cleansed by flood from the

---

167. Philippians 2:1-11.
168. Matthew 18:21-22.
169. Genesis 4:23-24.

sins of humankind that had multiplied, presumable through violence toward each other.[170]

Slaves in the Roman culture were dependent on the welfare of their masters. A slave who worked hard took care of himself by caring for the master. Jesus said it was the same for his disciples. Having completed all they were commanded to do for the sake of the Kingdom, they could happily say, "We are no more than unworthy servants; we have done only what we were told to do."[171] If we are partners-in-being, we cannot claim that our loving service is anything more than being ourselves.

Since children had no social status, his disciples thought it untoward that parents bother the Master by bringing children for a blessing. Jesus corrected his disciples, thus offering a new teaching. He said, "Let the little ones come to me, and do not prevent them; for the kingdom of heaven belongs to such as these."[172] He used the same title of "little ones" for the powerless and marginalized in society. Jesus taught that the powerless who placed their faith in God would inherit the Kingdom, and those whom he sent out to gather them into the Kingdom had their reward simply in doing so.

Jesus associated feeding the hungry with impeccable religious observance, since he said caring for the least prepared oneself to be welcomed into God's kingdom. While riches were seen by his culture as divine affirmation, he taught having riches made it hard to enter God's kingdom. Being poor meant being favored by God; being great meant serving others. Losing self was the path to finding self; accepting a child who had no power was accepting the power of God's Kingdom. He affirmed again and again that the material universe was filled with the abundance of God; everything we need is available if only we would share it. From his hands, a child's lunch

---

170. Genesis 5:28-29.
171. Luke 17:7-10.
172. Matthew 19:13-15.

of a few buns and some dried fish, for which Jesus gave thanks, fed thousands who ate and were filled.

His conviction as a faithful Jew was that God's very words give life. Jesus acted on that conviction by his participation in synagogue services, personal prayer in seclusion, and teaching his disciples to pray by calling God "Our Father."[173] What may be most amazing is that he prayed after his successes at preaching, miracle working, and healing, as well as before. Those focused on their own success pray beforehand; those focused on God being at work in their ministry pray all the more in gratitude and thanksgiving after they succeed.

Jesus proclaimed the way of the cross, boundless compassion expressed in forgiveness of sinners and love of enemies. According to the gospels, Jesus predicted his death multiple times. In particular, he said he would die by crucifixion, a Roman capital punishment which completely demeaned the human dignity of the one executed. Jesus invited his disciples to take up their cross and follow him, assuring them the way was easy and the burden light. He taught his disciples that the compassion one desires when suffering should be shown even toward those who cause the suffering. The perspective of Jesus stretched his disciples' understanding of themselves and of God.

Christic Conscious Expansion

In Jesus, his disciples encountered more than a person who could make them feel God's presence and power, as had Moses who gave the commandments and the prophets who taught fidelity to God's commandments. Encountering the humanity of Jesus, his disciples encountered God in an I-Thou relationship. After himself coming to faith in Jesus, the Apostle Paul made it clear that he had encountered the God of the Jews in a new way. He had encountered in Jesus someone whom God raised from the dead and who would come

---

173. Luke 11:1-4.

again to complete God's work. The work of God in Christ was a share in God's glory, the manifestation in creation of God's power and rule.[174] In Christ, God was revealing a new understanding of the material universe which through the humanity of Jesus was destined to share in the glory of God. This means Jesus was a cosmic event whose significance is on the order of a second Big Bang.

Pope Francis, in two letters to humankind, expressed the relevance of the teaching of Jesus for sustaining the environment (*Laudato Si!*) and for gathering together the human community in solidarity and collaboration for the just sharing of the gifts offered by fellow humans and Earth itself (*Fratelli Tutti*). Both letters describe practical expressions of self-emptying love for the sake of justice and peace among humans and for the sustaining of all Earth's ecosystems. The letters were published separately but are integral to each other, just as the story of life on Earth shows relationships among humans have become integral to sustaining all life-forms on Earth.

Christians believe we can encounter the creator-God through the humanity of Jesus the Christ, who is God incarnate, and learn how to live in a new way with each other and all life-forms. This is the gift Genesis says Adam and Eve refused. They hid themselves from encounter with God because of their shame in being less than God. Through Jesus the Christ, God is fulfilling what we now see was the original plan of salvation, which is the fulfillment of the Cosmos. It was always the plan of our creator to accompany us to the fulfillment of the divine goodness with which we were created. This will be accomplished in order to save us from our shame at being less than God, a shame which is the root of our sins. It will happen by a transcendence called *theosis*, the gift of becoming like God which is expressed through self-emptying love (*kenosis*). In Christ humankind has received a share in God's compassion. But to be fully received,

---

174. 1 Thessalonians 1 and 2.

compassion must be shared, as is seen in Christ who, himself being God's beloved Son, loved us to the end. And so, humans are to share compassion with each other and with the rest of creation through the same self-emptying love.

A non-biblical source around 112 C.E. mentions Christians singing hymns to Christ Jesus. A Roman governor in what today is Turkey wrote to Emperor Trajan asking for advice on how to deal with Christians. Pliny said in part that the Christians were in the habit of meeting on a certain fixed day before it was light, when they sang in alternate verse a hymn to Christ as to a god. Written twenty years before Pliny's letter, the Gospel according to John opened with just such a Christological hymn which proclaims that the man Jesus is the divine Word of God.[175] John tells us this was possible because Christ's divine status pre-existed his being human.

John introduces his Gospel with a hymn which begins, "In the beginning was the Word, and the Word was with God, and the Word was God. He was in the beginning with God. All things came to be through him, and without him nothing came to be."[176] The Word of God in eternal relationship with God was manifest in the creation of the Cosmos. The hymn goes on to say that this Word took flesh in the humanity of Jesus and empowered those who believe in him to become daughters and sons of God.

The other three Gospels, written about 40 to 50 years after his death, also proclaimed Jesus to be both human and divine. Matthew and Luke introduced their Gospel accounts of Jesus with stories of his divine conception and human birth. These stories have been told at Christmas through the centuries. Mark, the shortest of the gospels and reputedly the first written, deals with the divinity of Jesus in a completely different way. He begins by telling us the gospel is about Jesus Christ, the Son of God. However, in the gospel he withholds the declaration that Jesus is Son of God until his death on the cross.

---

175. John 1:1-17.
176. John 1:1-3.

Only then does the Roman centurion who witnessed the human death of Jesus proclaim him to be clearly the Son of God. There is a variety of perspectives within the New Testament on the person of Jesus the Christ. These are evidence that the language used to express belief in Jesus as the Christ and Son of God developed even in the first four decades after his death.

In letters written before Paul died in 62 C.E., he quoted their own hymns to the local churches. These hymns are evidence the first Christians believed in Christ's cosmic significance. The clearest example is found at Colossians 1:15-20 which states Christ is, "the image of the invisible God, the firstborn of all creation. For in him were created all things in heaven and on earth...He is before all things, and in him all things hold together."[177] Another hymn, Philippians 2:5-11, declares that before he became flesh, Jesus "was in the form of God [but] did not regard equality with God something to be grasped [clung to]. Rather, he emptied himself, taking the form of a slave, coming in human likeness."[178] The hymn goes on to proclaim that God named Jesus of Nazareth "Lord" (responsible for the completion of creation) because he humbled himself to death on a cross. In Ephesians 1:3-16, Paul gives an extended poetic discourse on the risen Christ's significance for the resurrection of our bodies in the Eschaton (the future fulfillment) and that the Spirit is the down payment against the full inheritance yet to come. In Galatians 3:1-6, he insists that it was through faith in Jesus crucified that the Christians have already received this pledge, the Spirit from God.

The descriptions of his death, although they vary somewhat among the four Gospels, unite in declaring Jesus is also the foundation of a new way of being-related among humans. Christ's *kenosis* (self-emptying in Greek) is creation's personal response to the creator's *ekstasis* in creating the Cosmos. Christ's self-emptying on the cross is the return of creation to the source of its goodness, and it is

---

177. Colossians 1:15-17.
178. Philippians 2:6-7.

the reason all creation will shine out like the children of God at his coming again.[179] The unique evidence of Jesus as Son of God, the Incarnation, consists in his fully pouring himself out in love. This is a capacity with which every human is created but because of sin does not fulfill. Jesus by virtue of his fulfilling this human capacity is not only uniquely the Incarnation of God in created matter (flesh), but he is also uniquely the one through whom we receive the Spirit of God that makes us sharers in divinity. He let go of being in the form of God and became as we are not simply for his own sake but for the sake of creation. As Word of God he brought creation into being. As the incarnate Word he is bringing it to fulfillment.

By raising him from the dead, God affirmed the witness Jesus gave in his earthly ministry and revealed him uniquely as beloved Son of God in whom his Father was well pleased.[180] Taking up his life again in the resurrection, Jesus confirmed his unique relationship to God. This filial affirmation took a unique form in his ascension. Jesus was exalted to the right hand of God as the Lord of creation.[181] His exaltation is the completion of his resurrection, a sharing in the Glory of God.

Since his humanity was completely poured out in his death, Christ's resurrection and ascension are the complete filling of his humanity with the power of the Spirit, so that through Christ others might be filled with the same Spirit of God and become daughters and sons of God.[182] At Christ's coming again in the Glory of God, the Parousia, the entire Cosmos will be completed by the power of the Spirit to share the glory of God as daughters and sons. Therefore, Jesus the Christ is called Lord, because he is responsible for the fulfillment of the Cosmos.

---

179. John 3:16-17 and St. Ambrose, letter #35. https://www.fourthcentury.com/ambrose-letter-35, accessed 9/18/2021.
180. Romans 1:4, "established as Son of God in power according to the spirit of holiness through resurrection from the dead, Jesus Christ our Lord."
181. Philippians 2:10-11.
182. Romans 1:4.

A letter in the New Testament to Jewish Christians offers yet another way of understanding the impact of the Incarnation on the Cosmos. The Letter to the Hebrews declares that Christ is the Son of God and as such surpasses the elemental powers that operate in the universe. Among Jews and other wisdom traditions at the time of Jesus, there was a belief that the powers of the universe were expressions of, or at least under the control of, spiritual forces called angels. These powers were like those about which Brian Swimme has written, but they also included the basic physical powers that modern science observes and tests. The Letter to the Hebrews says that Christ is superior to all these. Recalling that previously God had spoken in a variety of ways, the letter declares God now speaks to us through the Son. This Son,

> is the refulgence of [God's] glory, the very imprint of [God's] being, and who sustains all things by his mighty word. When he had accomplished purification from sins, he took his seat at the right hand of the Majesty on high, as far superior to the angels as the name he has inherited is more excellent than theirs. [183]

However,

> since the children share in blood and flesh, he likewise shared in them, that through death he might destroy the one who has the power of death, that is, the devil, and free those who through fear of death had been subject to slavery all their life.[184]

In his humanity, Jesus suffered death in self-emptying love and so removed death's power. The power of evil, or the devil, can no longer use death to motivate humans to make their own personal interests alone the measure good and evil. The measure is now the fullness of resurrection and life which fills the humanity of Jesus, who is the image of God in which humanity was created. Goodness is now

---

183. Letter to the Hebrews 1:3-4.
184. Ibid. 2:14-15.

revealed as the Spirit whom the risen Christ has poured out on Earth and its life-forms. Sharing divinity with us by that Spirit, Jesus is also guiding all the powers in the universe to their fulfillment by that same Spirit.

Conclusion

Teilhard de Chardin's vision of the cosmic nature of Christ drew upon the Christological hymns in the New Testament and upon his experience of Christ manifest in the Liturgy of the Eucharist. Teilhard completed his Mass on the World on August 6, the day in the Catholic liturgical calendar for the annual celebration of the Transfiguration of Jesus.[185] He used themes from this Christological event, a theophany or manifestation of God, as a template for his cosmic vision of Christ.

In that event, Jesus has gathered on a mountain with three of his disciples who will later witness his agony in the garden the night before he dies. Suddenly, Moses and Elijah are speaking with Jesus as a brilliant light transfigured him. Luke tells us they are discussing his coming passover in Jerusalem. Suddenly, a dark cloud covers the scene as God's voice is heard saying, "This is my beloved son, listen to him." Listening, of course for a Jew, means doing what is heard. His disciples are to repeat his self-emptying in their lives if they seek the same transfiguration into divine likeness.

Teilhard's vision in the Mass on the World was that the whole Cosmos will be transfigured by the glory of God, as was the humanity of Jesus on the mount. For Teilhard, the humanity of Jesus was both a part of creation and its universal particular. This means what happens in Christ will happen in the whole that is one in him. He is the one in whom God is revealing the fulfillment of the whole of

---

185. The Transfiguration of Jesus is found in Matthew 17:1-8; Mark 9:2-8; and Luke 9:28-36.

creation. The risen Christ is the Omega Point at which the entire Cosmos is to be transfigured, shining out with the divine glory.

The voice of God directed his first disciples to listen to Jesus, who had been explaining that he was going to be put to death and rise again in order to bring this work of God to completion. That message remains the source of Christian hope for the Cosmos in our day. When placed in dialogue with the new cosmology, it is the foundation for a whole new way of thinking about human life and the evolution of the Cosmos. This new way of thinking is what Teilhard believed would develop the Noosphere, the collective unconscious of the whole of humanity, in understanding the transcendence of the Cosmos brought about by Jesus the Christ and his self-emptying love. The next chapter will show how this understanding of Christ has evolved since Teilhard's death.

Chapter XII

Evolving Christology

Christological Grammar

In his book, *Christ the Heart of Creation*, Rowan Williams, the emeritus Archbishop of Canterbury and renowned Christologist, explains that at the heart of creation is not *something* about which we have unique information but *someone* who seeks encounter with us.[186] The title reprises Teilhard's 1908 *Le Coeur de la Matière* (The Heart of Matter), in which he said, "The universalized Heart of Christ coincides with the heart of Matter transformed by love."[187] Encountering his human heart gives humankind a unique experience of the transforming power of love. In that encounter, we can reject our false selves and accept both the fullness of truth about who we are in the Cosmos and who the Cosmos is in relation to God.

But Williams tells us that when we encounter God's love in the transformed heart of Christ,

> The Christological model requires us to think of non-duality in its proper sense: God and the world are not two things to be added together. Neither are they two things that are 'really' one thing. They exist in an asymmetrical relation in which one [Cosmos] depends wholly on the other [God], yet is fully itself, made to be and to act according to its own logic and structure [the fixed laws of nature].[188]

---

186. Rowan Williams, Christ the Heart of Creation (London: Bloomsbury, 2018).
187. Pierre Teilhard de Chardin, S.J., Le Coeur de la Matière (Paris: Seuil, 1976), 60. Translation provided by https://www.traditioninaction.org/Progressivist Doc/A_033_TeilhardHeartChrist.htm
188. Ibid., xiv, inclusion my own.

Williams calls this principle by a name he admits is an awkward phrase, "non-dual non-identity." This same non-dual non-identity is what Catholic doctrine declares about the humanity and divinity of Christ. His two natures are not mixed or confused but united in a single person, an experiencing self who is involved with Truth.

Williams' awkward phrase, non-dual non-identity, means that encounter with God, the divine, is not an encounter with *something* in any way like the Cosmos or any of its parts. God cannot be identified as any part or even the whole of the Cosmos. However, God is not incompatible with or limited from encountering creation, as if God must be isolated from creation. God is free to interact with anything God has created, and this divine interaction is not limited by the divine nature or the laws of created nature. Neither does God suspend the laws of the Cosmos in order to freely interact with any part of creation or with us humans in our personal encounters with God.

As Robert Russell indicated, the contingency within creation itself (things do not have to be the way they are) allows for this free interaction of God with all the parts of the Cosmos. Since the Cosmos was not created by God as a finished or complete product but evolves, Williams can posit that this free interaction of God with creation reveals God's promise that the Cosmos will find its fulfillment not in itself but in its ongoing encounter with God. The revelation of this promise, God drawing the Cosmos to its fulfillment, is available in any encounter with the person of Jesus the Christ. But that means we need to think differently about what it means to be human. With Christ we share a human nature capable of representing the whole material world in our encounters with and responses to God. But like Christ we also share the capacity to represent God in encounters with creation.

It should be evident that Williams contextualizes our understanding of Christ's humanity and divinity within personal encounter. Encountering Christ, we encounter both God who missioned him and creation to whom he was missioned. This is the current evolution of Christology. Whereas in the past, the tendency of Christology to favor conceptual thinking led to understanding our experience of Christ in the same way we experienced other persons and life-forms. All of these were simply things we experienced. Just so, we could think of God as a thing like other things but greater. This tendency is evident in the critique by Michael Wyschogrod of the concept of the Incarnation.

Wyschogrod explained why a Jew would reject the idea that the man Jesus was the enfleshment of the divine. Jews, he said, understand God can be located, accessed, by human encounter among a holy people or in a holy place. However, the idea that God was *incarnate* (made flesh), as Christians teach about Jesus, would for Jews annul the non-dual non-identity relationship of God with creation.[189] God would then be something, a man. This is a question Christians had to deal with once they became an officially recognized religion in the Roman Empire.

It took three hundred years after the death of Jesus before Christians were fully free to publicly practice their faith within the Roman Empire. Christians had become so numerous that their multiple grammars describing Christ's person became a source of discord among themselves and consequently in the civil society. For that reason, the Emperor Constantine asked their leaders to clarify the teachings from their scriptures that Jesus of Nazareth was both human and divine. At the Council of Nicaea (325 C.E.), the assembled bishops settled on some new language to explain their faith about Jesus the Christ.

The new grammar was logical assertion (claiming that something is the case). The Christian scriptures had used instead the grammar of encounter (the experience of a person or event). Scripture presented Christ's divinity as the experience of encountering Christ's

189. Michael Wyschogrod, "A Jewish perspective on incarnation," in Modern Theology, 12:2 April 1996, 195-209.

humanity in context of his mission among us. The New Testament described Jesus of Nazareth as the Son of God based on God's missioning him through the Spirit who overshadowed his virgin mother at his conception and then Jesus as an adult beginning his ministry.[190] The council of Nicaea used a different grammar (philosophical terms) to describe the relationship between divinity and humanity in the person of Jesus. The council used philosophical language instead of the grammar of encounter found in scripture. The council did so because Christians needed to enculturate the gospel, to speak so as to be understood within the predominant cultural worldview. At that time, the predominant cultural perspective was not encounter but Greek philosophy.

The council used philosophical language to profess faith in what the Christian scriptures taught. The scriptures taught that Jesus was both fully human and fully God, beginning with his conception by the power of the Spirit from the flesh of the Virgin Mary. The council members decided on a Greek word, *homoousios*, to clarify their faith that the man Jesus of Nazareth was "consubstantial" with the God of the Jews, whom Jesus called Father. That meant Jesus was of the same divine substance or essence as God while being fully human, without mixture or confusion of these two natures in his one person.

But by developing this Christological definition, the council also was teaching that the one God of the Jews was a Trinity. The council began the historic Christian clarification of God's self-revelation in Christ. This clarification continued through the centuries, describing the relational nature of God's being, a Trinity who was one God by their indwelling each other. Only the Word of God (the Son and Wisdom of God, the Second Person of the Trinity) became incarnate in Jesus of Nazareth. Therefore, the person his disciples encountered through his humanity was the pre-existing divine Son of God through whom all are drawn to be daughters and sons. His divinity

---

190. Luke 1:29-35, 3:21-22, and 4:14-21.

animated his humanity to fulfill his mission to complete creation. Jesus, then, is consubstantial with God, as the Son of God from all eternity.

Ever since Nicaea, Christian communities have used this normative Christological and Trinitarian language to describe the person of Jesus and the God he revealed. The Nicene Creed remains central to the faith of the Catholic and Orthodox Churches and for many Protestant communions. The importance of the term "consubstantial" is that it shows Christians believe, in encountering the person of Jesus, they are encountering the Word of God, by whom all things were made and through whom creation will find its completion. In this way, Christians clarified their faith by using philosophical grammar. The Father, Son, and Holy Spirit are each God and yet one God.

Contemporary Christology

While Teilhard was still living, advances in Christology were being made based on the theology of Saint John Henry Cardinal Neuman. His *The Grammar of Ascent* published in 1870 declared 1) that a subject or person is always situated in circumstances or in motion and, therefore, 2) our experience of a subject is always provisional. The whole of a person exceeds our experience of the person as a subject in relationship with us. We cannot simply abstract from what is known about the person in order to know her fully. Rather, we perceive each person in a manner Neuman called "illative." This means that to know a person truly, we make inferences from our full experience of the person, which includes the self-experience of the person herself and the experience of her by others.[191] Consequently, theologians gradually became aware that abstract formal logic is not the fullness of human knowing. Christology cannot ultimately be

---

191. Newman's writing influenced the theology of Karl Rahner, SJ, and Hans Urs van Balthasar, both of whom in turn contributed to the Second Vatican Council and subsequent Christological clarifications.

reduced to a formal system of thought about Jesus, like that expressed in the term "consubstantial." That would make him a thing, not a person. Christology is always a response to a person, Jesus the Christ, and his concrete relationship with those who encounter him.[192]

Of course, Rabbi Heschel reminded us that God takes the first initiative in every encounter. It is in encountering us as creatures that God exercises the divine freedom to make the creator known in creation. God-seeking-us is what Heschel proclaimed to be the central issue in our existence. In the Jewish tradition, God called Abraham and his descendants into encounter so that through them God ultimately might prepare a personal encounter for all humankind. The Jews, as one people, were to struggle to be faithful to God as God was faithful to them. Thus, they were to give example of how all humankind could recognize our capacity for *hesed*, faithful love of God and neighbor. The Jewish myth of the sin of Adam and Eve set out the basic purpose of this human struggle, that creation grow into the likeness of God. Our reinterpretation of that myth in previous chapters was our attempt to clarify its meaning and so clarify the struggle.

The Creator used the laws of nature in this universe to evolve humankind in a world where suffering and death already existed. It was this suffering and death that humans chose to use against each other. Instead, God's plan was that suffering and death would lead to a reemergence of life through a love that leads to fullness of life. Christians, in their encounter with the person of Jesus, inferred that he was gathering the suffering of the world to fullness of life by his ultimate act of love, his death on a cross. In Jesus the Christ, the Heart of the Cosmos, they perceived God holding the history of all the suffering of humankind and of every sentient being.

---

192. Mark McInroy, Online symposium, "Ressourcement and the reception of Newman in twentieth century theology,", National Institute for Newman Studies (Pittsburgh, PA), March 11, 2021.

As part of the Cosmos, the humanity of Jesus is the domain of emergence in which suffering and death transcend to the fulfillment the Creator promised to the Cosmos. What made this possible for Jesus? The Christian answer, according to the scriptures, is that his humanity is one with the Word by which God made all things. Jesus, the Incarnation, is God seeking us in a human way. Being the Word of God, he can represent God in an encounter with us and the rest of creation. Being human, he can represent us and the whole Cosmos in an encounter with God.

It is reasonable to ask, how can two natures, one human and the other divine, exist as a single person. According to Maximus the Confessor (580-662), a nature, or what something is, can be made actual, or become a person, by a power or agency which is not exclusively its own. The Word of God being one with God does not exclusively belong to Jesus as if he merited, by the perfection of his humanity, to be God. As St. Augustine taught in "A Treatise on the Predestination of the Saints," the incarnation of the Word in the person of Jesus was a grace (a gift) given him by God at his conception for the sake of the rest of creation. This gift was given so that through him we might share in God's divinity by a similar gift or grace.

In the cosmology of Maximus the Confessor, God's creative power is a kind of self-emptying. This analogy does not mean God loses some part of God, but that God does not simply keep life in abundance just for God. God's self-emptying, or *ekstasis* in Greek, brought forth the Cosmos. God shared existence with what was created. The act of divine *ekstasis* in creating the Cosmos is, by analogy, called "speaking." As Genesis says, "God spoke and it came to be." A divine speech-act is what is meant by the Word of God, and the Word spoken from all eternity by God is God. Theologian Sallie McFague, in *A New Climate for Christology*, explains that *kenosis*, or self-emptying, which we see evident in the universe, helps us understand the self-emptying of God in creation and in Jesus on the cross.[193]

Put contextually, Jesus shared the human nature of his first disciples. They could, therefore, pick him out in a crowd as the carpenter from Nazareth. However, what made him who he was, his personhood or unique existence, was that in encountering his person, one encountered the Word of God, and through an encounter with him could experience the working of the Spirit of God, God's going out in love or *ekstasis*. In creating the Cosmos, God's *ekstasis* through the Word initiated an encounter with a created "other" to whom God gave being. That "other" is the wholeness of the Cosmos, with its many and diverse parts, which God continues to sustain through the working of the Word and the Spirit. As the new cosmology teaches, the created universal powers of cataclysm and emergence are a self-emptying of creation through which life emerges. God's love was so evident in the death of Jesus on the cross (cataclysm in nature) that the centurion who was standing nearby proclaimed him to be the Son of God (the emergence in our humanity of the fullness of life).[194]

A new understanding of God was revealed in creation by the death of one of its parts. In the death of Jesus, the power of cataclysm brought about a new kind of emergence. Through Christ's resurrection others could share the same "filiation" with God through his Spirit.[195] By encounter with the divine emptying in the person of Jesus the Christ, other human beings experienced a new capacity for communion with God, receiving and returning this self-emptying love through Christ and in the Spirit. For us to care for and live responsibly in right relationship with Earth and its creatures, while at the same time having compassion for those who inflict

---

193. Sallie McFague, <u>A New Climate for Christology: Kenosis, climate change, and befriending nature</u> (Minneapolis: Fortress Press, 2021).
194. Mark 15:39.
195. John 1:12 and 2 Corinthians 3:17.

suffering upon us, is to model God's heartbeat at the center of the Cosmos, Christ the Heart of Matter.

The Incarnation

Some proponents of cosmology speak of God being incarnated in the Cosmos or of Earth as the body of God. They appear to do so because they want to emphasize that if one part of creation is divine then all the Cosmos must be also. However, by doing so they risk collapsing the difference between being created in the image of God and coming to fulfillment in likeness to God. The Incarnation of the Word of God in Jesus has significance in the new story of creation. The New Cosmology is a philosophy of nature, and the Catholic doctrine of the Incarnation clarifies how nature is in the image of God and its capacity for divine transcendence or likeness with God.

Thirteen centuries ago, Maximus the Confessor wrote that there is a difference between having a human nature and being a human person. He explained whatever we share with others in creation belongs to our nature (human). However, an irreducible uniqueness belongs to each personal existence, to one's personhood. Humans share much with each other and with other creatures, but each person's being is unique and personal. To be a person is to have a unique way of existing, not a unique nature. Each human person is a human nature existing as a unique self. And our unique existence always evolves in our relationship with other persons. Modern science confirms his explanation of the human person and human development.

A newborn infant is human. Her mother also understands that she is a separate person. But a newborn does not know the uniqueness of her own existence as a person among others. At birth, she experiences herself and her mother as one wholeness. Evolution, however, has provided the infant with the means of developing her personhood, her existence as a unique self. That development begins with the aid of mirror neurons. Mirror neurons are a class of neurons that register activity, whether the infant's own motor activity or when she observes a similar activity performed by another individual.

As her mother makes cooing sounds, the infant begins to copy the sounds, and the path opens to finding her own voice and articulating it in speech. As her mother gazes into her face and smiles, the infant mirrors the smile, and the path to being a unique person among other persons is opened. The child develops a unique relationship with her mother through these mirrored behaviors. As the infant's existence or personhood develops, she is able more fully to express her humanity by recognizing her mother is a different self from her. Over time, she will manifest her own unique self in a wider community, in all her relationships with others. Thus, she becomes more truly herself, more completely a person in communion with the whole to which she belongs. This becoming more truly a person, a free agent in communion, is exactly what is hampered by the consequences of the original sin.

Boethius, a philosopher in the sixth century C.E., defined a person as *an individual substance possessing a rational nature.* From there grew our current complex social discussions about what it means to be a person based on our rational abilities, what our culture calls an individual. An "individual" is someone living out a role, like an actor among other actors. In fact, *persona* was the Latin word for the mask an actor wore to assume a role. Playing a role requires a cunning willfulness because an actor is not a free agent in her relationships. Instead, she must conform to the role she is playing. This same lack of freedom afflicts any "individual" who pursues her own interests and, consequently, will experience herself in contention with the other actors in society.

But the idea of "person" as a free agent in communion with all that exists only developed as Christians clarified their understanding of the person of Jesus. He is the divine person whose self-emptying love in becoming human and in suffering death in his humanity offers us the freedom to be in communion with God and all creation. The idea of a person as "a uniquely free personal existence lived in communion" arose with Christianity, according to John Zizioulas, an Orthodox theologian and bishop.[196] Jesus, the man from Nazareth, is the revelation of such a divine existence, a person in communion with God and all creation. In communion with him, the New Adam, we become persons who are free agents in communion with all that exists, partners-in-being with God and with all creation. Christ is the model for our being created in the image of God and the model for our struggle to enter into likeness with God.

We already have spoken about the human capacity to be partners-in-being through encounter. Encountering Christ in a communion of self-emptying love is what frees our human capacity, so that we can be involved with the truth of our being. Communion in self-emptying love is the matrix for being a person, a partner-in-being. Christian theologians reflected on the death of Jesus and saw there the self-emptying love of God which is bringing creation to its fulfillment. Likewise, they recognized that the Spirit, who is the love with which God loved the Son and raised him from the dead, now is given to those who believe in Christ.

The gift of the Spirit brings a person into communion with Christ who is the New Adam, the first truly free human agent in communion with God and all creation. Being in communion with Christ, our will is freed to love others as God loves us. This way of understanding who God is named the Economic Trinity, because it is how Christians understand God working for the good of the whole of the Cosmos. Such an expansion of human consciousness throughout the world is what Teilhard envisioned would bring the Cosmos to fulfillment in Christ.

Christ is the one who fulfilled for humanity the two great commandments, to love God with our whole self and our neighbor

---

196. John D. Zizioulas, Being as Communion: Studies in personhood and the church, Contemporary Greek Theologians Series, No 4 (Yonkers, NY: St Vladimir's Seminary Press, March 1997).

as ourself. Through encounter with him we can develop our full human potential to be like God revealed in Christ. Maximus clarified the important difference between image and likeness. He taught that image is the beginning, but likeness is the fulfillment. The full maturity of our human nature can only develop in our relationships with God, self, and others. That maturing of our existence is called holiness, sharing likeness with God in whose image we were made. But the transformation of our human personhood into divine holiness takes place through struggle. It is the struggle to use well our evolved human traits, which come to us from our human ancestors and their precursors among earlier life-forms on Earth. That struggle is to mirror for the sake of all creation the actions of God, which we both glimpse in creation and receive as a gift in our communion with Christ through his humanity now transformed by his divinity.

This is the truth to which Christ gave witness in the world, the Truth that Christ is. This truth consists in the real satisfaction of our desire to be persons-in-relationship with all that is. But it is a satisfaction that is not already fully actualized. Rather, it is a satisfaction which can be tasted now in our communion with Christ, but which ultimately will be fully actualized when it is fulfilled for the entire Cosmos.[197]

For the present, if we are to act as God acts in the Cosmos, we must mirror the divine self-emptying love which we see in the numinous fully revealed in Christ. We can do so by benevolently caring for each other in the human community and for other life-

---

197. This understanding of the now and not yet definition of truth is compatible with the pragmatic theory of truth developed by Charles Sanders Peirce (1839–1914) found in "A Neglected Argument for the Existence of God", Hibbert Journal, 7: 90–112; reprinted in Collected Papers of Charles Sanders Peirce (Volumes V and VI), Charles Hartshorne and Paul Weiss (eds.), Cambridge, MA: Harvard University Press, 1935, pp. 311–339. And it is a philosophy of Truth that is more compatible with the Christian Scriptural meaning of Truth, than is the old Greek definition that truth is the correspondence between things and our ideas of them.

forms in the world. This mirroring of self-emptying love is animated in us by the Spirit. The Spirit is the divine power that interacts freely with us and the whole universe, so that created things may evolve in likeness to God. Christ's resurrection is the revelation of God's intent for the universe to transcend itself in that way. The Spirit is the power within the universe to fulfill its promise as the Spirit fulfilled Jesus the Christ in his resurrection from the dead.

What is irreducible for each person (personal existence as oneself) is available to that person as a vision of self. That vision can be the measure by which to make our personal choices. But a self-vision or ego is most often associated with what clouds a person's vision of herself, thus resulting in a *gnomic* or calculating will. If her vision could be clarified, her will would be freed to follow that clarified vision of herself in her relationships.

In Christology, the humanity of Jesus the Christ is understood to have had just such freedom of will. His vision of his personhood was clarified in his union with the eternal Word of God. The Word was the mirror for his human ego to glimpse the truth about his person. This clarity of self-awareness was provided by the Word of God who was united with his humanity as one person. This is known as the "hypostatic union." That union, however, did not annul his human struggle to perceive and respond to the divine vision. This is self-evident in the agony of Jesus in the Garden of Olives on the night before his death, in his struggle during his ministry with the expectations of his culture, which was highlighted in his temptation in the desert even before his ministry began, and by his faithfulness to prayer as he sought God's will for him.

The risen Christ now shares his clarified vision with other humans. Jesus is the mirror into which we can look to see our truest self. His Spirit is the power at work in us to choose what we see in him as the truth about ourselves. Sin may be inevitable, but it is not necessary if we cooperate with the vision of self we see in Christ and the power of the Spirit that is at work among us. Through Christ we can find a vision of our true selves as the daughters and sons of God. Through the Spirit's power we can act in our relationships with others and indeed with all creation according to the self-emptying love that we see at work in the Cosmos. The struggle to clarify our vision of self is what Christians call living the qualities (virtues) that we see in Christ as we encounter him. But, if he is two natures in one person, divine and human, can we humans actually become like him?

In his cosmology, Maximus taught "each created substance [existence] is a participant in and reflection of the eternal Word; all *logoi* [signs in the cosmos] subsist in the Logos [the eternal Word of God]."[198] A contemporary translation might be the following. All codes or laws in the universe, such as genetic codes for living creatures, or quantum mechanics which governs the composition of subatomic particles, or the cosmic powers of cataclysm and emergence can only be recognized because they exist in particular things or interactions within the Cosmos.

Only when a code manifests in or between things can that code be recognized. For example, the power of allurement manifests in the attraction between things, whether as gravity or as love. As such, allurement can be recognized as a power that permeates the universe and each of us. Material sciences say that nothing exists outside of these cosmic codes or laws and their manifestations. While acknowledging these codes (logoi) exist in all creation, Christians say that God revealed the Logos (Word), the pattern for everything else that exists, in the person of Jesus of Nazareth, the Incarnation. But how can we exist like him who is both human and divine?

Each part of creation exists as it is coded by the divine Word who is the Cosmic Code, the source of seamless generativity in the universe. The truth of each thing that exists is its capacity for likeness with the Eternal Word which has encoded it. Jesus the Christ is that

---

198. Williams, 120.

Word made flesh, the human manifestation of the Code (Logos), who encodes all creation and through whom all creation will find the fulfillment of its truth. Nevertheless, if the Word of God is encoded in all created things, it would be understandable to want to talk about God being incarnated in the Cosmos, not simply in the person of Jesus. However, that would be to collapse the difference between being created in the image of God and coming to fulfillment in likeness with God.

Rowan Williams' phrasing for the difference between creation and God, "non-dual non-identity," and Maximus speaking of Christ as the *Logos*, both preserve the ancient Christian faith that Jesus the Christ is a unique person within the Cosmos. He is 1) the one whose humanity revealed God in a new way, 2) so that through communion with him we may become free agents in our expression of self-emptying love, 3) through which creation will be brought to fulfillment by Christ and those in communion with him. This is the unique significance of the Incarnation for the fulfillment of the Cosmos.

Conclusion

This chapter has focused on the uniqueness of Christ amidst creation's encounter with the creator. That encounter takes place in a created material world that reflects the image of God yet is not God. We humans are created in the image of God, and we can grow into God's likeness. The risen and exalted Christ is the image in which we are created and the fulfillment of creation. As a person who shares both God's divinity and our humanity, Jesus is the mirror in which we glimpse our true selves. The Spirit of God, the power of *theosis* or divinization, is at work in those who entrust themselves to this truth of our being.

In the early twentieth century, Teilhard de Chardin was trying to make clear the place of Christ in the evolution of the Cosmos from its beginning to its completion. Christ's uniqueness as God and man is essential to the vision expressed in his writings. Jesus the Christ is both divine and human. As the eternal creative Word of God, Jesus the Christ is Alpha, the beginning of all created things and their pattern for fulfillment. Through self-emptying love he became as we are and poured himself out on the cross out of love for God. As such, he is the host, a consecrated offering in worship of God. His offering is himself. Through his human nature Jesus is that part of the Cosmos whose response to God's self-emptying in creating the cosmos is a self-emptying love. Thus, he is the one who is bringing creation to completion, its Omega Point. As such, Christ is the Cosmic fulfillment, the one who is drawing all to likeness with God. The final chapter will reflect on the resurrection of Christ as the vision for the fulfillment of the Cosmos, its Omega Point.

Chapter XIII

The Fulfillment

Living the Questions

In 1903, a military academy student began sending some of his verse to the famous poet Rainer Maria Rilke (1875-1926) seeking his opinion. Rilke's responses were published posthumously in *Letters to a Young Poet*. One of his more famous comments to the young man was,

> Be patient toward all that is unsolved in your heart and try to love the questions themselves ... Do not now seek the answers, which cannot be given you because you would not be able to live them. And the point is, to live everything. Live the questions now. Perhaps you will then gradually, without noticing it, live along some distant day into the answer.[199]

Rilke's response to the young poet would be equally good advice to us young *Homo sapiens*. As a species, we are only 300,000 years old. We have inhabited Earth for a mere fraction of its 4.5 billion years, which in turn is only a third of the existence of the Cosmos. Yet, because we evolved with the ability to be self-reflective, we have many questions. In this chapter we look at some of our questions about the Eschaton, the absolute future of our existence and that of Cosmos. We end this book with the hope that gradually, even without noticing it, we will live along into the answers. Of course this means that our understanding of time itself influences what it means to live into the answers we seek.

---

199. Rilke, Rainer Maria, Letters to a Young Poet. Accessed 4/11/22 at https://www.csus.edu/indiv/o/obriene/art206/Readings/rainer-maria-rilke-letters-to-a-young-poet.pdf

In *God after Einstein*, John Haught shows how Einstein's contributions to modern science made time an essential dimension of the evolution of our material universe. He says previous attempts to live into the answers we sought were by and large personal journeys of contemplative enlightenment, a kind of

> ...liberation from matter and time. After Einstein, however, we may at last envisage the whole universe as the primary drama and thus locate our personal spiritual pilgrimages, and even our religious traditions, inside the larger narrative of cosmic awakening in real time.[200]

In real time for instance, the mystery of the superabundance in the universe "liberates it from sheer necessity."[201] There is more of everything present in the Cosmos than we could ever consume. Time's arch itself bends toward awareness, thought, and most importantly toward compassion. Therefore, the excess of both life and thought on Earth is the ground for human stories that lead, not simply back to what has been, but toward the unfolding mystery of what may yet be. Mystery, abundance, and excess are the stuff of theological reflection on the last things. And as Haught explains, the perspective of modern science was blind to this narrative.

In *Cosmology from Alpha to Omega*, Robert Russell suggests science and theology, especially Christology, can benefit by becoming dialogue partners in their search into the absolute future of the Cosmos. It is beyond the scope of the current chapter to discuss the mutual influences and possible topics for this dialogue, which Russell develops at the conclusion of his book.[202] However, one example is important to note here. One feature of Christology, from its beginnings in Christian scriptures to this age, is that Christ will come

---

200. John Haught, <u>God after Einstein, What's really going on in the universe</u> (New Haven: Yale University Press, 2022), 47-48.
201. Ibid., 59.
202. Russell, Chapter 10, "Resurrection of the Body, Eschatology, and Cosmology: Theology and science in mutual interaction," 298-327.

again to complete his mission of salvation for the whole of the Cosmos. His new presence, Parousia, will complete creation. In other words, according to contemporary Christology, the Cosmos never existed in a steady state but has been always moving toward its fulfillment through Christ.

Until Einstein, however, science continued to hold that the Cosmos eternally existed in a steady state. Even Einstein had difficulty with the full implications of his theory of space-time, for instance that stronger gravitational attraction made time slow. But his calculations showed that theology's insight into time, that the universe had a beginning and is moving toward some end, is scientifically valid.

As we here conclude our dialogue between science and theology, we shift our concern to the end-time, the end of human life on Earth and the end of the Cosmos. These two are not the same for science, but for Christian theology they are frequently conjoined. Scientific eschatology, a dimension of ongoing astronomical research, focuses on questions about the physical end of the Cosmos and how human life might be preserved in the meantime. Christian eschatology focuses on the telos, or ultimate end toward which human life and the Cosmos are moving. That telos is the purposeful fulfillment for which all things were made and to which God is drawing them in the great drama of an unfolding universe.

Physical Eschaton

Current scientific knowledge indicates that roughly 5 billion years from now, the Sun will exhaust the hydrogen fuel in its core and start burning helium, forcing its transition into a red giant. During that shift, its atmosphere will expand out to somewhere around one astronomical unit, which is the current average Earth to Sun distance. All life on Earth will be incinerated. If humankind has not ventured to live beyond Earth, it will cease to exist, as will all Earth-based life-forms. Our species may cease to exist over the next five billion years anyway because of some other natural or intentional cause. If not, we will certainly continue to evolve, since we previously evolved from other species in less time. However, further human evolution, while it can be variously imagined, remains uncertain.

Until recently, there were two divergent scientific theories about the end of the Cosmos as a whole. Both theories presented the far future of the Cosmos as bleak. In 1912, Henrietta Swan Leavitt wanted to establish how quickly other groups of galaxies were moving away from our Milky Way galaxy and its group. She began by measuring the brightness of stars in our galaxy called Cepheids and compared their brightness to Cepheids in other galactic groups. Based on the comparative brightness of Cepheids amongst these groups, her findings showed that the Cosmos will continue expanding for another 500 billion years or more. Over that vast period, all the stars will gradually flicker out. The Cosmos will end in cold darkness.

Based on those results, the theoretical physicist Freeman Dyson, in his 1985 Gifford lectures, imagined how life could continue in that darkness. He asked his audience to imagine human thought detached from a human body and embodied in networks of superconducting circuitry, or even in an interstellar dust cloud. That was Dyson's version of eschatology, life existing as organized data in total darkness at near absolute zero. Robert Russell calls any theory of the survival of disembodied life "physical eschatology." There is more than one version.

Frank Tipler, another physicist, proposed a very different theory of the end of the Cosmos, fire rather than ice. He based his theory on measurements of the background radiation in the universe which was left over from the Big Bang. That method shows the cosmic expansion rate is slower than Leavitt's method found. If the Cosmos were expanding at this slower rate, Tipler believed, the galaxies eventually would contract together and the Cosmos would end in a fiery implosion. What would remain would be an infinitely small, hot, and dense mass. Nevertheless, Tipler thought we might be able to develop computers that would continue life digitally after Earth's demise until the contraction of the Cosmos was complete. Thus human thought would be extended by physical means for hundreds of billions of years beyond the end of Earth.

In July 2019, a Carnegie Institution news release revealed a third method for measuring cosmic expansion. This method produces data that provocatively falls in the middle between the two previous theories that predicted the end of the Cosmos in either ice or fire.[203] If this third method proves accurate, a new speculative future for the Cosmos will perhaps be developed, as a yet different kind of physical eschatology.

The question remains, why would physicists want to continue human life as disembodied thought? Dyson regarded the human mind as the source of religion, and he said environmentalism was the secular religion that was replacing socialism in his day.[204] Because the human mind can comprehend itself to some degree, Dyson believed the human mind was the best expression within the Cosmos of what God would be like, if there were a God. So, he created a thought experiment. If we could imagine our minds advancing beyond our own present ability to comprehend our thoughts, it might be the best

---

203. Carnegie Science (Pasadena, CA, July 16, 2019), "New Measurement Of Universe's Expansion Rate Is "Stuck In The Middle,'" https://carnegiescience .edu/news/new-measurement-universes-expansion-rate-stuck-middle, accessed October 13, 2021. Measurements comparing the brightness of nearby Cepheid stars to those in other galaxies indicate the expansion rate of the universe is 74.0 kilometers per second per megaparsec, and it will end in cold darkness. Measurements based on background radiation left over in the Cosmos from the Big Bang indicates its rate of expansion is 67.4; and, therefore, the Cosmos will end in fiery collapse. According to the recent red giant method for measuring the universe's expansion, the rate is 69.8—falling provocatively between the two previously determined numbers. If it's real, the red giant discrepancy could herald something new in the future of the Cosmos.
204. Freeman Dyson, https://libquotes.com/freeman-dyson/quotes/religion, accessed October 13, 2021.

and only part of life in the Cosmos that could continue without bodily form.

Much to the contrary, Tipler believed that, using current physics, Christianity itself could be shown to be an experimentally testable science.[205] For instance, in Tipler's explanation of creation, the singularity that was the source of the Big Bang was the act of God creating the Cosmos. Like Dyson, Tipler understood that human thought is the Cosmos reflecting upon itself, and the emergence of human thought in the universe signaled a unique evolutionary moment. That moment, human presence, could be preserved and perhaps advanced by artificial intelligence even after Earth and humankind were no more.

Neither physicist, Dyson nor Tipler, believed the age of the Cosmos (13.8 billion years) was sufficient to allow the random development even of amino acids, much less the evolution of *Homo sapiens* who have multiple capacities for thought. The emergence of human thought occurred in an unusually short time after life appeared on Earth; it was less than 4 billion years. It appeared to both scientists that human thought, the basis for the scientific method itself, was worth preserving in some form, even disembodied. Both Dyson and Tipler wanted to preserve that emergence in digital form and advance it, if possible, for as long as technology was able. The vast time period, between the end of life-forms on Earth and the physical end of the Cosmos, could allow for the evolution of our consciousness, whatever that may become once embodied in digital form.

Decades before these theories, Richard Bucke (1837-1902) had posited that our personal consciousness would someday evolve into cosmic consciousness, which he understood to be a kind of direct

---

205. Frank J. Tipler, The Physics of Christianity (NY: Doubleday, 2007).

knowledge of the organic wholeness of the universe as divine.[206] As a result of that evolution, he believed religions would become unnecessary because the existence of God would be self-evident to our cosmic consciousness. In the first half of the twentieth century, the writings of Teilhard de Chardin were filled with similar expressions of cosmic consciousness, a consciousness of the Cosmos as the work of God in Christ. His Jesuit formation taught him to find God revealed in all things.

While Bucke imagined that in the future humans would suddenly be caught on fire with an all-enveloping awareness of the wholeness of the Cosmos, Teilhard believed the divine fire of love manifest in Christ had already caught the whole universe on fire. A second Big Bang had taken place in the Incarnation, so that the fire of divine love now is gathering all to one in the Cosmic Christ.[207] This allowed Teilhard to see in science and in diverse religious traditions the effects of that divine fire.

His vision of an ongoing evolution of cosmic consciousness, the Noosphere, continues to be part of the new story of creation among Catholic proponents of cosmology. However, in their presentation of such an evolved human consciousness, some Catholic writers seem to suspend the unique effect of Christ on this cosmic evolution. Instead, they collapse the fundamental distinction between God and creation that underlies the development of Christology. Some are moved to do so because of their concern that religious claims to truth about God are exclusivist.

In this post-modern age, we are reminded that absolute truth cannot be exclusively claimed by any human system. We are always, whether science or theology, working within a horizon of knowing

---

206. Richard Maurice Bucke, <u>Cosmic Consciousness, The evolution of the human mind</u> (UK: White Crow Productions, 2011). Originally published in 1905 by Innes & Sons, Philadelphia.
207. Teilhard's vision expresses Paul's in Colossians 3:11, "Here there is not Greek and Jew, circumcision and uncircumcision, barbarian, Scythian, slave, free; but Christ is all and in all."

and not knowing. Christian eschatology bases its claims about the future of the Cosmos on the truth revealed in the beauty and goodness of the Cosmos through the resurrection of Jesus Christ from the dead.

The Resurrection

Christian anthropology posits that human life exists not simply as thought but as the totality of a person in communion with other persons. This totality includes body, mind, spirit, and relationships with the rest of creation and its creator. As such, human life is already emerging to another degree of fulfillment, whose signs are present, but whose completion remains beyond the horizon of our understanding. The signs of our future completion present now are the many forms of human compassion that have increased over the millennia of human evolution, even in the face of conflict and death. Christian eschatology is concerned with exactly that progressive emergence of compassion/self-emptying love.

Christianity proposes that the incarnation of God in the person of Jesus the Christ reveals God in a new way. As John Haught puts it, "God is not an 'eternal now,' detached from time and matter, but a compassion that gathers up, heals, transforms, and saves everlastingly whatever happens in time."[208] Thus the resurrection of Jesus is the fulfillment of divine compassion. He laid down his life freely out of love and was given the power to take it up again, as the divine revelation of the fullness of created life. Now creation waits for him to reveal his glory (Parousia) as the compassionate fulfillment of the whole universe.

As the universe is an arena of both continuity and discontinuity, the Christian Scriptures present the risen Jesus as a demonstration of continuity and discontinuity. These are expressed in the transcendence of his concrete humanity into the likeness of God

---

208. Haught, 180.

through his resurrection and exaltation. His resurrection is of eschatological significance for human life and for the Cosmos as a whole. Christ's bodily resurrection signals the eventual transformation of the entire natural world of which the humanity of Jesus is a part. From the point of view of Christian eschatology, the resurrection of Jesus is a proleptic event, an event that is a future reality present now in his risen person. It foreshadows the New Creation in which the dead are raised to new life and all creatures, as daughters and sons, look upon the face of God and have life to the full.

In the Gospels, his crucifixion, death, and burial are witnessed by others. This is a declaration that he lived and died like any other human. Since the body of Jesus was a human body, it was the sacrament of his personal presence and the symbol of the mystery of his personhood. Christ's resurrection, therefore, is initially indicated in each of the four Gospels by his empty tomb. The empty tomb may be interpreted in two ways, as a declaration of his bodily resurrection and as the basis for subsequent experiences of his risen presence by his disciples. The empty tomb then is not a proof of resurrection but a demonstration that what was buried, a lifeless corpse, is not who the risen Jesus is. Nor does his resurrection constitute a simple memory of a person important to his disciples.

The emptiness of his tomb points to something unique that happened after his death. Immediately after discovering the empty tomb on the morning of the third day, his disciples on the same day began to experience the risen Jesus. The living person his disciples had encountered during his earthly ministry was present to them once again. However, he was more than resuscitated, he was changed.[209]

---

209. At the time of Jesus, Jewish factions had diverse explanations for what happens after a person's death. The Pharisees believed in resurrection of the body because without a body, a person was no longer who she was in life since the body of each living thing is the symbol of a unique existence. Jewish Christians believed in the resurrection of the body, and this especially because of

The Gospels demonstrate the continuity of his person: 1) in his eating with them, which no ghost would do, 2) in the wounds of crucifixion which were manifest in his risen body, and 3) in his reminding them that he had told them repeatedly during his ministry that he would die and rise again.

The discontinuity, the change brought about by resurrection, is indicated 1) by his appearing and disappearing even in places where the doors are locked, 2) by his appearances on the same day in multiple distanced locations, 3) by his ascension/exaltation, and most provocatively 4) by his bestowing on his disciples the Spirit of God.

---

the resurrection of Jesus. But what happens to the person between death and resurrection?

Plato, a Greek philosopher who predated Christ, taught that the soul was a spark of divine life that had been trapped in the material body. The soul was set free by death and continued to exist after the death of the body. That explanation strongly affected Christian explanations about what happened to the soul after death and before resurrection. Aristotle, who post-dated Plato, taught that the soul was simply the life force animating a particular material substance. The soul was not something but an animating power. As such, a soul no longer existed after the death of the body it animated.

Late medieval Christians who used Aristotle's philosophy to explain other aspects of their faith, continued to use Plato's explanation of the immortality of the soul to support the Christian belief in resurrection. It otherwise would have been difficult to explain how the soul could exist after death without a body to animate. Thomas Aquinas theorized that perhaps the soul simply clings to God until the resurrection of the body, which is a wonderfully comforting belief for those who remain behind.

Christian biblical faith began to be codified into credal statement about 300 years after Jesus. These creeds proclaim faith in the resurrection of the body, not in the transmigration of a soul to heaven. It is the resurrection of the body, at the second coming of Christ, in which Christians believe and for which they hope. However, because theology, like science, is always working within the horizon of what we know and do not know, the Catholic doctrine or teaching about our immortal soul is used to support the doctrine of the resurrection of our body.

The idea of an immortal soul neither explains nor contradicts resurrection of the body. It simply helps give some reasonable explanation to what happens to a person while she waits for resurrection. Since the inauguration of relativity theory, some have proposed that since time is a feature of a material universe, God's action is not limited by time. The wait for resurrection, accordingly, might not be a matter of time at all.

At his baptism in the Jordan, Jesus had received in his humanity the Spirit of God, the anointing that began his ministry of setting people free. After his resurrection and ascension, he bestowed the Spirit on his disciples, missioning them to go among the peoples forgiving sins, a power belonging solely to God.

Christ's ascension is presented in Christian scriptures as the completion of his resurrection. His ascension or exaltation is his return to God who missioned him but does not mean he ceased to encounter his disciples. The last biblically recorded appearance of the risen Christ occurred post-ascension to Paul. In his encounter with the risen Jesus, Paul was changed to become a partner-in-being with Jesus. He was converted from being a persecutor of the Jewish disciples of Jesus to become himself an apostle of the gospel sent to the gentile nations. Instead of the end of his presence on Earth, the ascension of Jesus proclaims his power to bring his mission to fulfillment. In the ascension of Jesus, the glory of God is revealed more clearly than in the beauty, goodness, and truth of creation. As a part of creation, Jesus, now glorified, is transcendent in the fullness of divine likeness. The whole creation, of which Jesus is a part as a human, can now share in his glory as God, through this glorified Son of God who is drawing all creation to its fulfillment in God.

The Book of Revelation, the last of the Christian books of the Bible, paints an apocalyptic picture of the end of the Cosmos. It begins with these words of the glorified Christ, "Do not be afraid. I am the first and the last, the one who lives. Once I was dead, but now I am alive forever and ever."[210] The book goes on to imagine how the entire heavens and Earth will be changed through the risen Christ, described as the Lamb who was slain and now shares God's throne. His resurrection is presented as a corporate act, God initiating humankind into a new way of being alive as partners-in-being through the Lamb who was slain.

---

210. Revelation 1:17-18.

Similarly, we saw the Apostle Paul present Jesus as the new Adam. In Adam all experienced death, in Christ all will experience resurrection.[211] Since he has risen, all now have hope of resurrection and eternal life. In his letter to the church at Rome, Paul declared Jesus, "descended from David according to the flesh, but established as Son of God in power according to the spirit of holiness through resurrection from the dead."[212] Paul called him the fulfillment of the promises made to the Jews and names him Lord, having God's fullness of power over all creation. According to the Christological hymns in Paul's letters, the risen Jesus is the universal particular in whom the whole of corporate humanity is being shepherded into a new way of being, the *ecclesia* (the gathered). This communion with each other in Christ signals the transformation of the entire Cosmos into Christ's way of being one with God, his compassion revealed in his self-emptying love.

Asked what to make of the risen body of Jesus, Brian Swimme said,

> I think the resurrected body is coextensive with the cosmos; it isn't a loss of identity; it's actually like a new hue or a new tone. Similarly, the presence of the resurrected Jesus in a certain sense is everywhere. It's still a focused identity; yet it's coextensive with the entire cosmos.[213]

The risen Jesus is certainly a concrete personal identity. His risen bodily existence is also the telos, the ultimate end, of creation. All creation is to be transformed into the likeness of his risen body, and so he now lives coextensively with the whole of creation. Jesus is now

---

211. I Corinthians 15:20-25.
212. Romans 1:3-4.
213. U.S. Catholic, "Where does your faith fit in the cosmos?" Editors' interview, June 1997, 6. Accessed October 13, 2021, at http://www.fergusreilly.org/An_Tairseach/Theology_&_Ecology_files/Where%20Does%20your%20Faith%20fit%20in%20the%20Cosmos.pdf

Lord of the Cosmos having plenipotentiary power to bring creation to its completion in God.

That is why Russell agrees that the risen Jesus is, therefore, a proleptic event. Prolepsis is the presence now of something that is only achievable at the end of a project. The bodily risen person of Jesus of Nazareth is the prolepsis of the Cosmos at its fulfillment. In him, that fulfillment is already present in the drama of the continuing evolution of the Cosmos. And yet the risen Jesus does not simply exist within time as we know it, nor in some state of being beyond time that we may imagine as eternity. As the Resurrection and the Life, he exists in the incomprehensible being of God, beyond the horizon of our ability to fully comprehend his meaning. His way of being, likeness to God in our humanity, is the unfolding drama within the universe awaiting fulfillment.

Fulfillment, Now and Not-Yet

During his earthly ministry, Jesus was obedient to God, the essence of human love. Our contemporary understanding of obedience, "to do what I'm told," does not help us understand either divine love or the depths of human love. Rather, to be obedient begins with listening, having an open ear and a heart free to respond. Obedience, ultimately, is becoming what one hears and carrying it to completion. Obedience is an act of love, an act by which a person becomes a reflection of the truth she has heard in her encounter with her beloved. This understanding of obedience is especially important if we are to understand what it means to say that Jesus "was obedient even unto death on a cross."[214]

The creator, by creating a material universe, allowed all life to be subject to physical death. On Earth, humans made death an instrument to accomplish our own desires, especially through random victimization. Jesus, in his obedience to the laws of nature

---

214. Philippians 2:8.

and our human vulnerability to moral evil, was by his death the emergence of a new way of being alive to the love of God. His death was foreshadowed in the struggle of the Jewish people to be as faithful to God as God was to them, especially in their exile and return. In Christ's acceptance of death out of love of his Abba, the power of resurrection was already present, not in the quantifiable amount of his suffering but in his love of God and us amid his suffering. His death in time, out of love of God, constituted a way of life that mirrored the eternal compassionate self-emptying love he received from God. Thus, Jesus was revealed as the eternally poured-out Son of God, like-in-being to God's eternal *ekstasis*.

Christ's self-emptying love or *kenosis* was illustrated in the gospels according to Matthew and Mark, when from the cross he prayed the twenty-second psalm which begins, "My God, My God why have you abandoned me." The psalm goes on to describe his condition of suffering and concludes with his placing his hope in God. The prayer illustrates his power to lay down his life and his power to take it up again. As he prays, a bystander describes our doubts, "Let us see if Elijah (the Jewish precursor of the Eschaton) comes to help him."[215]

After his death, the Roman centurion witnessing the same kenotic event declared aloud what had been revealed by his death, "Truly this man was the Son of God!"[216] Sallie McFague wrote beautifully about the centrality of Christ's kenosis, his self-emptying love, and its impact on our efforts to combat climate change by befriending both each other and the whole of nature. Christ's self-emptying was for the life of the world and revealed the intent of the creator, our partnership with God in the fulfillment of the Cosmos.

Christ's suffering and death is not presented in the Christian scriptures as an isolated experience of a single person. His death is an event of encounter and, therefore, communion with others. Through these encounters both Jesus and the community of his disciples find

---

215. Mark 15:36.
216. Mark 15:39, Matthew 27:54.

new ways of being. Simon from Cyrene assisted in carrying the cross of Jesus, and Mark mentions Simon's sons by name because they were recognizable members of the post-resurrection church.[217] In the Gospel according to Luke, Jesus promises that he and one crucified with him will be together in paradise that same day.[218]

The evangelist John presents one of the last acts of Christ's self-emptying. Jesus hanging on the cross entrusts the care of his mother to his beloved disciple and the disciple to the care of his mother. This act of Jesus establishes the *ecclesia*, the gathering or church, a gathering in mutual love of those who believe he laid down his life in love for God and us. Thus he completed his mission from God to complete humankind and all creation. As Mary and the beloved disciple gaze upon him, he returns their gaze. Through their encounter in mutual suffering, Christ and the church represent each other and have compassion for each other. In their encounters with him as the crucified and risen Lord, his disciples become partners-in-being in love of God, a new way of being. But one that is yet to be fulfilled, as the first letter of John says. "Beloved, we are God's children now; what we shall be, has not yet been revealed. We do know that when it is revealed we shall be like him, for we shall see him as he is."[219]

These encounters give some clue about the universe's fulfillment, what it means to be like God. Each creature fulfilled (resurrected) as its own self, each indwelling the other, all sharing one life in Christ with God, who is all in all. [220] Our current understanding of the interdependent nature of the Cosmos and its seamless generativity will be completed as a wholeness beyond its present reality. The indwelling will not be simply with each other but also with God. Creation begun in the image of God will be creation fully alive in likeness to God. For this reason, Jesus is called Lord, the one

---

217. Mark 15:21.
218. Luke 23:40-43.
219. I John 3:2.
220. I Corinthians 15:28.

223

responsible for creation's fulfillment. This is because "in him were created all things in heaven and on earth, the visible and the invisible, whether [the concrete existences or their manifest powers]; all things were created through him and for him."[221] That is why, when he laid down his life, all died in him and all have come to life again in him.[222]

Conclusion

The Book of Revelation uses an image from Genesis to describe how the new creation will be the union between the risen Jesus and his disciples. Like a man who leaves father and mother and clings to his wife to become with her one flesh and bone, Jesus is the Bridegroom and those gathered with him, the Bride. The Bride, and the Spirit who indwells her, cry out for Christ to come again, and bring all creation to its fulfillment.[223] This is more than a new hue or tone within the Cosmos, it is a wholly new and unexpected emergence from the cataclysm of the death of God Incarnate upon the cross. The Book of Revelation expresses this emergence as a new heaven and a new Earth. These take the place of the former heaven and the former Earth which have passed away, and even the sea will be no more.

In its eschatological vision, Revelation pictures God declaring, "Behold, I make all things new."[224] The continuity in this vision with the current material condition of the universe is that the powers of cataclysm and emergence operative among us will be manifest in Cosmic completion. The discontinuity is that there will be no more cataclysm, no more death. However, as Orthodox theology proclaims, that does not mean no more emergence. As Maximus the Confessor taught Christians to expect, the peace of

---

221. Colossians 1:16 ff.
222. 2 Corinthians 5:14-15, inclusion my own translation.
223. Revelation 22:17.
224. Revelations 21:1 and 5.

heaven will be an eternal adventure of discovery of self and each other in the immensity which is God.

Here we glimpse a second pattern for the fulfillment of the Cosmos. The "something new" that has come about is not simply a new perspective on the world but a new way of being the world. If we see suffering and death through the lens of Christ's cross, we will experience an "overview effect" in which humankind can be reconciled to each other, and to Earth and its creatures.[225] The old way of life, the way of protecting ourselves against death by causing other humans and even Earth to die, gives way to something new. As Rene Girard taught, the death of Jesus is the good news that no more random victimization is necessary. One person has died so no other persons need ever to be put to death. Instead, in Christ all may have life and life in abundance.

However, the path to this fulfillment is the very struggle Jesus spoke of. It means presently embracing suffering, especially in our encounters with each other. In that embrace, we will be able to express compassion rather than competition, and together become partners in befriending the whole of nature. The Spirit of the risen Jesus is given to us for this very purpose. The Spirit is God's breath testifying in us to God. The Spirit of the Beloved Son in us empowers us to live as beloved daughters and sons of God.

There is now no suffering that is greater than the life at work in us. Which means we now have the strength to enter the struggle for the good of the whole of creation. We can grow in hopeful expectation of what we will yet be, and this expectation now bears the fruit of endurance in our care for Earth's creatures and each other in the human family. This is what Genesis says we were created to do. Now God has empowered us through the *kenosis* of Jesus to do it in a wholly new way. Not in fear of death and vulnerability, but

---

225. 2 Corinthians 5:16-18.

with the assurance of the transcendence already emerging in us and the whole Cosmos through Jesus the Christ.

References

Allison, James. The Joy of Being Wrong: Original sin through Easter eyes (NY: Crossroads Publishing, 1998).

Alison, James. Faith beyond resentment: fragments catholic and gay (NY: Crossroads Publishing, June 2016).

Ambrose, Letter #35, https://www.fourthcentury.com/ambrose-letter-35 accessed 9/18/2021.

Arbuckle, Gerald. Violence, Society and the Church: A Cultural Approach (Collegeville, MN: Liturgical Press, 2004).

Barrick, Audrey. "Stephen Hawking Explains Creation, Big Bang Sans God," The Christian Post, August 8, 2011. https://www.christianpost.com/news/stephen-Hawking-something-out-of-nothing-is-possible.html accessed April 20, 2021.

Bartholomew, His Beatitude, "Global Responsibility and Ecological Sustainability," Closing Remarks, Halki Summit I, Istanbul (June 20, 2012), quoted in "Laudato Si!", note 18.

Benedict XVI, "Caritas in Veritate," June 29, 2009, https://www.vatican.va/content/benedict-xvi/en/encyclicals/documents/

Benedict XVI, Homily of His Holiness, Aosta, Italy: July 24, 2009, https://www.vatican.va/content/benedict-xvi/en/homilies/2009/documents/hf_ben-xvi_hom_20090724_vespri-aosta.html

Bergson, Henri. Creative Evolution, trans. Arthur Mitchell (Mineola, NY: Dover Publishing, 1907).

Berry, Thomas. The Dream of the Earth (Berkeley: Counterpoint Press, 2015).

Berry, Thomas. The Great Work (NY: Belle Tower, 1999).

Bower, Bruce. "Israeli fossil finds reveal a new hominid group, Nesher Ramla Homo," Science News, June 24, 2021.

https://www.sciencenews.org/article/israel-fossil-new-hominid-nesher-ramla-homo-human-evolution accessed July 30, 2021.

Bucke, Richard Maurice. Cosmic Consciousness, The evolution of the human mind (UK: White Crow Productions, 2011). Originally published in 1905 by Innes & Sons, Philadelphia.

Cann, R. L. "Mitochondrial DNA and Human Evolution," Nature, January 1987.

Carnegie Science, "New Measurement Of Universe's Expansion Rate Is "Stuck In The Middle," https://carnegiescience.edu/news/new-measurement-universes-expansion-rate-stuck-middle accessed October 13, 2021.

Cosolmagno, Guy, S.J. "What the story of Galileo gets wrong about the church and science," America, October 2020.

Dallas, Kelsey. "Cosmic humility: The spiritual side effects of viewing Earth from outer space," Deseret News, July 27, 2015. https://www.statesboroherald.com/churches/faith/cosmic-humility-the-spiritual-side-effects-of-viewing-earth-from-outer-space/ accessed January 21, 2022.

Dunne, John, C.S.C. The City of God: A study of myth and mortality (NY: Macmillan Co., 1965).

Dyson, Freeman. https://libquotes.com/freeman-dyson/quotes/religion accessed October 13, 2021.

Fairly, Margaret, R.S.M. Just Love: A framework for Christian sexual ethics (NY: Continuum International Publishing Group, 2006).

Girard, Rene. Evolution and Conversion: Dialogues on the origin of culture (London: Bloomsbury, 2008).

Gibbs, John C. Moral Development and Reality: Beyond the theories of Kohlberg, Hoffman, and Haidt, Fourth Edition (NY: Oxford University Press, 2019).

Giere, Ronald N. "The Perspectival Nature of Scientific Observation," June 3, 2015. https://www.researchgate.

net/publication/242574702_The_Perspectival_Nature_of_ Scientific_Observation accessed October 24, 2020.

Haight, Roger, S.J. Jesus, Symbol of God (Maryknoll, NY: Orbis Books, 1999).

Hamilton, Edith. Witness to the Truth: Christ and his interpreters (NY: W.W. Norton, 1962).

Haught, John. God after Darwin: A theology of evolution (Boulder, CO: Westview Press, 2000).

Haught, John. God after Einstein, What's really going on in the universe (New Haven: Yale University Press, 2022).

Hayes, Christine. What's Divine About Divine Law? (Princeton: University Press, 2015).

Heschel, Abraham Joshua. God's Search for Man: a Philosophy of Judaism (NY: Farrar, Straus, Giroux, 1955).

Hopkins, Gerard Manley, S.J. "As Kingfishers Catch Fire."

Horgan, John. "Remembering Big Bang Basher Fred Hoyle," Scientific American, April 7, 2020. https://blogs.scientific american.com/cross-check/remembering-big-bang-basher-fred-hoyle/ accessed April 20, 2021.

Jayaram V. "Hinduism and the Belief in one God." https://www.hinduwebsite.com/onegod.asp accessed April 20, 2021.

Klein, Terrance W. https://www.americamagazine.org/faith/2021 /03/31/scripture-reflection-catholic-good-friday-homily-lent-240359 accessed 4/2/2021.

Klein, Terrance W. Vanity Faith: Searching for Spirituality among the Stars (Collegeville, MN: Liturgical Press, 2009).

Kruger, Elias. "Integrating Technology and Religion in a Post-Secular World," a post on AI Theology, https://www.aitheology.com/2021/02/17/integrating-technology-and-religion-in-a-post-secular-world/ accessed October 25, 2020.

LaCugna, Catherine Mowry. God for Us: the Trinity and Christian life (San Francisco: Harper, 1991).

Louth, Andrew. Maximus the Confessor (NY: Routledge, 1996).

May, Gerald, M.D. Will and Spirit: A contemplative theology (NY: Harper Collins Publishers, 1982).

McFague, Sally. A New Climate for Christology: Kenosis, climate change and befriending nature (Minneapolis: Fortress Press, 2021).

McInroy, Mark. Online symposium, "Ressourcement and the reception of Newman in twentieth century theology," National Institute for Newman Studies (Pittsburgh, PA), March 11, 2021.

Peirce, Charles Sanders. "A Neglected Argument for the Existence of God," in Collected Papers of Charles Sanders Peirce, eds. Charles Hartshorne and Paul Weiss (Cambridge, MA: Harvard University Press, 1935).

Pilch, John J. The Cultural World of Jesus, Sunday by Sunday, Cycle B (Collegeville, MN: Liturgical Press, 1996).

Pope Francis, "The Church Does Not Grow Out of Proselytizing … It Grows Out of Attraction," Christian News Network, December 24, 2019.

Rappaport, Margaret Boone and Corbally, Christopher J., S.J. The Emergence of Religion in Human Evolution (NY: Routledge, 2020).

Rolheiser, Ron, O.M.I., "The Cosmic Christ," https://ronrolheiser.com/the-cosmic-christ/ accessed July 10, 2020.

Russell, Robert John. Cosmology from Alpha to Omega: The creative interaction between theology and science (Minneapolis: Fortress Press, 2008).

Sawicki, Marianne. The Collected Works of Edith Stein, in Philosophy of Psychology and the Humanities (Volume 7) (ICS Publications, February 2016).

Smith, Jeremy A. "The Science of the Story," Greater Good Magazine, June 8, 2016. https://greatergood.berkeley.edu/article/item/science_of_the_story

Sparado, Antonio. "Reflections on 'Fratelli Tuti'," La Civilta Cattolica, October 8, 2020.

Swimme, Brian and Berry, Thomas. The Universe Story: From the primordial flaring forth to the Ecozoic era, a celebration of the unfolding of the cosmos, (San Francisco: Harper, 1992).

Swimme, Brian "The Universe Is A Green Dragon," in The New Story, Winter 1985/86. https://www.context.org/iclib/ic12/swimme/ accessed October 20, 2020.

Teilhard de Chardin, Pierre, S.J. Hymn of the Universe (NY: Harper & Row, 1961), https://d2y1pz2y630308.cloudfront.net/5520/documents/2016/10/The%20Mass%20On%20The%20World.pdf

Teilhard de Chardin, Pierre, S.J. Le Coeur de la Matière (Paris: Seuil, 1976). Translation https://www.traditioninaction.org/ProgressivistDoc/A_033_TeilhardHeartChrist.htm

Thich Nhat Hanh, Going Home: Jesus and Buddha as Brothers (NY: Riverhead Books, 1999).

Tipler, Frank J. The Physics of Christianity (NY: Doubleday, 2007).

Tucker, Mary Evelyn, Grim, John, and Angyal, Andrew. Thomas Berry, A Biography (NY: Columbia Press, 2019).

U.S. Catholic, "Where does your faith fit in the cosmos?" Editors' interview, June 1997. http://www.fergusreilly.org/An_Tairseach/Theology_&_Ecology_files/Where%20Does%20your%20Faith%20fit%20in%20the%20Cosmos.pdf, accessed October 13, 2021.

van Beeck, Franz Jozef, S.J. Christ Proclaimed: Christology as Rhetoric (NY: Paulist Press, 1979).

Williams, Rowan. Christ the Heart of Creation (London: Bloomsbury, 2018).

Wyschogrod, Michael. "A Jewish perspective on incarnation," in Modern Theology, 12:2 April 1996, 195-209.

Zizioulas, John D. Being as Communion: Studies in personhood and the church, Contemporary Greek Theologians Series, No 4 (Yonkers, NY: St Vladimir's Seminary Press, March 1997).

About the Authors

Richard Chiola is a priest of the Catholic Diocese of Springfield-in-Illinois. He is a former professor of both graduate theology and counseling therapy, and a retired sexual addiction therapist. He holds a M.Div., M.A.s in Religious Studies and in Human Development Counseling, and a doctorate in Historical Theology. His publications include <u>Catholicism for the Non-Catholic</u> (Templegate, 2006).

Sister Sharon Zayac, O.P., is a member of the Dominican Sisters of Springfield, Illinois, and cofounder and past director of Jubilee Farm, the community's 164-acre eco-spirituality center. She holds a degree in secondary education and master's degrees in both hospital administration and Earth Literacy. Her publications include <u>Earth Spirituality: In the Catholic and Dominican Traditions</u> (Sor Juana Press, 2003).